Hands On Social Studies

Grades 5-6

Table of Contents

U.S. Constitution

The Preamble

Concepts

- The Constitution created the United States central (federal) government.
- The Constitution set up a system of laws that would govern all people in the United States.
- The Constitution was meant to protect the rights and welfare of all United States citizens.
- The authors of the Constitution intended for it to last generations.
- The Constitution established protection for the rights of the states.

Objectives

- To know why the Constitution was written
- To understand that the Preamble is an introduction to the Constitution
- To understand the intent of the authors of the Constitution

Vocabulary

union, republic, ordain, preamble, common defense, posterity, welfare, domestic tranquility, justice, democracy; Note: Federal, central, national and United States are interchangeable when used to identify the type of government we have.

Preparation

Obtain one large reproduction of the Constitution or make copies from an almanac or encyclopedia.

Background Information

Before the Constitution was written, the Articles of Confederation were the first national form of government for the original 13 states. However, the Articles proved to be very weak. They did not call for an executive branch of government or for a system of national courts because the states did not want these. The Articles of Confederation established a congress, but at the same time, allowed each state to pass its own laws and ignore those passed by the Congress. The Articles did not work because the states had as much, if not more, power as Congress.

It was obvious to some that a stronger central government was needed. So, leaders from five states met and proposed that the Articles be revised. On that recommendation, the Constitutional Convention convened May 25, 1787. Almost four months later, on September 17, 1787, after many arguments, discussions and compromises, the new Constitution was signed by thirty-nine of the fifty-five representatives who had met in Philadelphia with the intent of revising the Articles of Confederation.

Teaching Suggestions

- Questions for Discussion - Ask students the questions below to see how much they already know about our Constitution and what they would like to learn.

  What do you think school would be like without any rules?

  What do you think traffic would be like without any regulations?

  Who makes up our central government?

  How are these people chosen?

  What do you think our country would be like without a strong central government?

  What do you think the qualifications should be for someone holding a position in the Federal government?

- Go over the Constitution with the class. Point out its three sections (the preamble, articles, amendments). Explain that the articles clearly define the legislative, executive and judicial branches and their duties, the states' roles, and amending and ratification of the Constitution, but it will not be their responsibility at this time to know specifically what the content of the articles is.

- Discuss the vocabulary words with the class.

- You know your class best. You may want to read and discuss the preamble together. Divide into small groups or have students do page 3. *The Preamble*, individually after a thorough discussion of the vocabulary. Whichever method you select, distribute the worksheet. Read it through together once to see if there are any questions.

- Follow-up: Write a class constitution.

  Begin with a preamble that tells what the document will accomplish. Then set down rules: Who is in charge? What powers do they have or not have? What are their duties?

2

U.S. Constitution

The Preamble

Name _____

The first sentence of the Preamble to the Constitution could be written simply, "We the people of the United States do ordain and establish this Constitution for the United States of America." But between "We the people of the United States" and "do ordain ....." are six reasons explaining why the Constitution was written. Read the Preamble below and write what the six reasons for its establishment are after each "To" below the Preamble. Then write what each reason means and give an example of why it is included or what it is meant to accomplish or prevent.

> *We the people of the United States, in order to form a more perfect Union, establish justice, insure domestic tranquility, provide for the common defense, promote the general welfare, and secure the blessings of liberty to ourselves and our posterity, do ordain and establish this Constitution for the United States of America.*

Reasons for establishment of Constitution:

To _____
_____
_____

To _____
_____
_____

To _____
_____
_____

To _____
_____
_____

To _____
_____
_____

To _____
_____
_____

U.S. Constitution

The Bill of Rights

Concepts

- Everyone has rights.
- The Bill of Rights was added to the U.S. Constitution to protect the rights of every U.S. citizen.
- Twenty-six amendments have been added to the Constitution as times have changed.
- The Constitution may be updated by amending it.

Objectives

- To understand everyone has rights
- To know what rights are
- To understand what the Bill of Rights is and why it was added to the Constitution
- To understand how and why amendments have been added to the Constitution and how they can be added in the future

Vocabulary

ratification, Federalist, Anti-Federalist, amendment, petition, indictment, militia, enumeration, quorum, concurrence, reprieves, emoluments, tribunals, insurrections

Preparation

- Make enough copies of the U.S. Constitution (from an encyclopedia or almanac) for your class.
- Cut out newspaper articles that are affected by or could affect the Bill of Rights.

Background Information

Once the Constitution was signed by the delegates at the Constitutional Convention, it had to go to the states for ratification. Those opposed to the Constitution (the Anti-Federalists) argued that they would lose their individual rights. Those who favored the Constitution (called Federalists) had the same concern but felt a strong government should be established first to protect the people's lives, freedom and property. The Federalists wrote letters to newspapers and made speeches to convince the states to approve the Constitution as it was written. They said it could be amended to include the rights the people wanted. Several states approved the Constitution with the understanding that a bill of rights would be added as soon as possible.

And so, they were. Once the nine states needed to ratify the Constitution had approved it, the Constitution became the law of the land. A President and Congress were selected by the method outlined in the Constitution. The Bill of Rights was the first order of business when the new Congress met. James Madison led the new Congress in the proposition of twelve amendments. Ten of them were ratified by the states. These first ten amendments are called the Bill of Rights.

Teaching Suggestions

- Distribute copies of the U.S. Constitution to the students. Briefly go over each article with students so they get a feel for what the main body of the original document covered, and why a Bill of Rights was necessary. Point out how the first three articles not only say who may hold office, but that the three branches of government check one another and keep any one branch or persons from becoming too powerful. Article IV deals with states' powers and Article VI puts the Constitution first after debts are paid. Article V and Article VII deal with the ratification of and amendment of the Constitution.

- Begin by going over the Bill of Rights (the first ten amendments) with the students. Ask some of the following questions:
  1) What are the five freedoms protected by the first amendment?
  2) Which amendment guarantees the right to a speedy trial?
  3) Which amendment restricts cruel and unusual punishments?
  4) Which amendment guarantees the right to have a gun?
  5) Which amendment guarantees the right of a person's privacy?
  6) Which amendment do you think is the most important? Why?

- Tell students that the Bill of Rights was not originally part of the Constitution. Ask if they think it was needed and why. Ask if they think all of the amendments are still needed.

- Show students (or have them find) news articles that contain material that may either affect or be affected by the Bill of Rights (i.e. Rodney King police brutality trial, gun control, etc.).

- It probably is best to do the three sections of page 6. B*ill of Rights* separately. Start

The Bill of Rights continued

with the first two sections after the students understand what purpose the Bill of Rights serve. Cut the page into three sections. Distribute each section as you want the students to do it.

Section 1: School Bill of Rights: Students may work individually or in small groups on this section. When they are finished, have all ideas presented. Vote on them. Make copies of the ten that receive the most votes. Have students read them to other classes and leave a copy with the teacher.

Section 2: Personal Bill of Rights: Students should work individually on this section. Let consenting students present their ideas of what they believe their rights should be to the class. Have each student take his/her list home and discuss it with his/her family.

Section 3: New Amendment: Before doing the last section, the class should know that amendments may be, and have been, added to the Constitution as times have changed. Go over Amendments XI - XVI so they are aware of those that have been added since the Bill of Rights.

Ask some of the following questions:

1) How many amendments have been added to the U.S. Constitution?

2) Amendments XIII - XV are sometimes called the Civil Rights Amendments. Why?

3) Which amendment is the only one to have repealed another and which one did it repeal?

4) Which amendments have changed voting procedures? How have they changed them? Why?

• Discuss with your students any ideas they have for an amendment that should be added to the Constitution. Present news articles if anything is currently being considered. Distribute the last section. Have students write what they believe is a necessary amendment to the Constitution. They could write a letter to one of their representatives in Congress suggesting it, too.

Notes/Ideas for Next Time

U.S. Constitution

The Bill of Rights

Name _____

Write a bill of rights for your school. _____

_____

_____

_____

_____

_____

_____

_____

_____

_____

_____

Write a personal bill of rights. _____

_____

_____

_____

_____

_____

_____

_____

_____

_____

_____

_____

_____

Write an amendment you would like to see added to the U.S. Constitution. _____

_____

_____

_____

6

U.S. Constitution

Three Branches at Work

Concepts

- The United States Constitution calls for three branches of government: the executive, legislative and judicial.
- Each branch has specific duties.

Objectives

- To know the three branches of the federal government and their duties
- To understand how the branches check one another

Vocabulary

Congress, legislature, impeach, tribunal, naturalization, apportionment, veto

Preparation

Make enough copies of the first three articles of the Constitution for every student.

Background Information

The United States Constitution created three branches of government: the executive (to carry out the laws), the legislative (to make the laws) and the judicial (to decide when laws passed at the federal, state and local levels follow the constitution or not). Each branch acts as a check on the other.

Teaching Suggestions

- Read the first three articles of the Constitution together. Read one article at a time. See that students understand who comprises each group and what each group's duties are.
- Draw three columns. Write one heading - Legislative, Executive, Judicial at the top

of each one. List the specific duties of each branch.

Legislative	Executive	Judicial

- Ask students which branch is most representative of the nation and of the state and why.
- Ask students to explain how each branch is kept from becoming too powerful.
- Tell students that recently, some states have voted to limit the number of terms their congressmen and congresswomen may serve. Ask how students feel about this and why.
- Tell students that many state governments have an item or on-line veto. The United States government does not. Ask if they think it should. Have students give reasons for their responses.
- Have students bring in news articles relating current proceedings of the three branches.
  (1) Discuss them as a class.
  (2) Post them on a red, white and blue bulletin board entitled **U.S. Government at Work.**
  (3) Make copies of one or more for every student. Ask students to write a response to one or more of the following questions:
  - How would you vote and why?
  - What do you think the President will do and why?
  - If the law passes and is approved by the President, do you think the Supreme Court will challenge it and

why?
  - If the President vetoes the law, do you think he/she is within the right of the law and why?
- Invite your district's representative to speak to your class.
- Compare your United States Constitution with your state constitution.

Notes/Ideas for Next Time

_____
_____
_____
_____
_____
_____
_____
_____
_____
_____
_____
_____
_____
_____
_____
_____
_____
_____
_____
_____
_____
_____
_____
_____
_____
_____
_____

U.S. Constitution

Three Branches at Work

Name _____

Write what you would do as a member of each branch of government in regard to the "law" being proposed.

> **Law under consideration:** The penny would no longer be a coin in the U.S. monetary system. Everything would cost five cents or more.

As a member of Congress: _____

_____

_____

_____

As President: _____

_____

_____

_____

As a judge on the Supreme Court: _____

_____

_____

_____

> **Law under consideration:** Every company with ten or more workers must hire the same number of men and women.

As a member of Congress: _____

_____

_____

_____

As President: _____

_____

_____

_____

As a judge on the Supreme Court: _____

_____

_____

_____

8

U.S. Constitution

Three Branches at Work continued

Name _____

> **Law under consideration:** The first Monday of every other month beginning in February 1997 will be a national holiday. No other holidays will be observed.

As a member of Congress: _____

_____

_____

_____

As President: _____

_____

_____

_____

As a judge on the Supreme Court: _____

_____

_____

_____

> **Law under consideration:** All schools in the United States must be open for students' attendance the same number of days. They will open on the first Monday after August 24th and will close the first Friday after June 5th.

As a member of Congress: _____

_____

_____

_____

As President: _____

_____

_____

_____

As a judge on the Supreme Court: _____

_____

_____

_____

A Point of View

Map Making

Concepts

- A picture of an area is usually drawn while in it or at the side of it.
- A map is a drawing of an area usually done from the air.
- A map is a diagram of an area with representations of its features.
- A map shows the location of specific points in a specific area.

Objectives

- To understand the difference between a realistic picture and a map
- To recognize realistic images and symbolic ones
- To draw a realistic picture and an aerial representation of the same space

Materials

shoe box, step stool, photographs (See Preparation.)

Vocabulary

cartographer, aerial view, point of view, diagram, perspective, symbolic, representative

Preparation

Take pictures of several scenes or objects from different points of view.

Background Information

An artist usually sits at the edge or to the side of a scene he or she creates. A mapmaker usually takes photographs from the air of the surface he or she intends to diagram in map form.

Teaching Suggestions

- Place a shoe box on a surface in view of all students. Ask them to sketch the box from their seats. Then, have them, one at a time, stand on a stool and look directly down on the box. Have them draw the box from this vantage point. Discuss the differences.

- Show the photographs you took (See Preparation.) to your students. Ask them to say from where (in relation to the picture) you took each photo.

- Ask a student to draw a tree on the board. Ask another student to draw a building, and ask a third student to draw a person. Ask three other students to show on the board how they would draw a representation of each on a map (from the air).

- Pair students up. Distribute page 11. *A Point of View.* Have students read it. Answer any questions they might have. When they understand what they are to do, instruct them to take turns drawing each other from two points of view.

- Have students define the vocabulary words and use them in a story they write about a search for hidden treasure.

Notes/Ideas for Next Time

Map Making

A Point of View

Name _____

- In the space below, draw your partner sitting at his/her desk in the classroom.
- Draw the part of the classroom walls that you can see from where you are while drawing your partner.
- Make an "X" at the approximate spot from where you made the drawing.

Imagine being suspended from the ceiling.
Draw the shape (walls) of the classroom. Example:

1. Show a square-shaped room by drawing four lines of equal length on each side.
2. Leave spaces where there are windows and doors. Label them.
3. Write FRONT where the front of the room is located.
4. Draw your partner's desk where it is located in the room. Draw your partner at his/her desk.

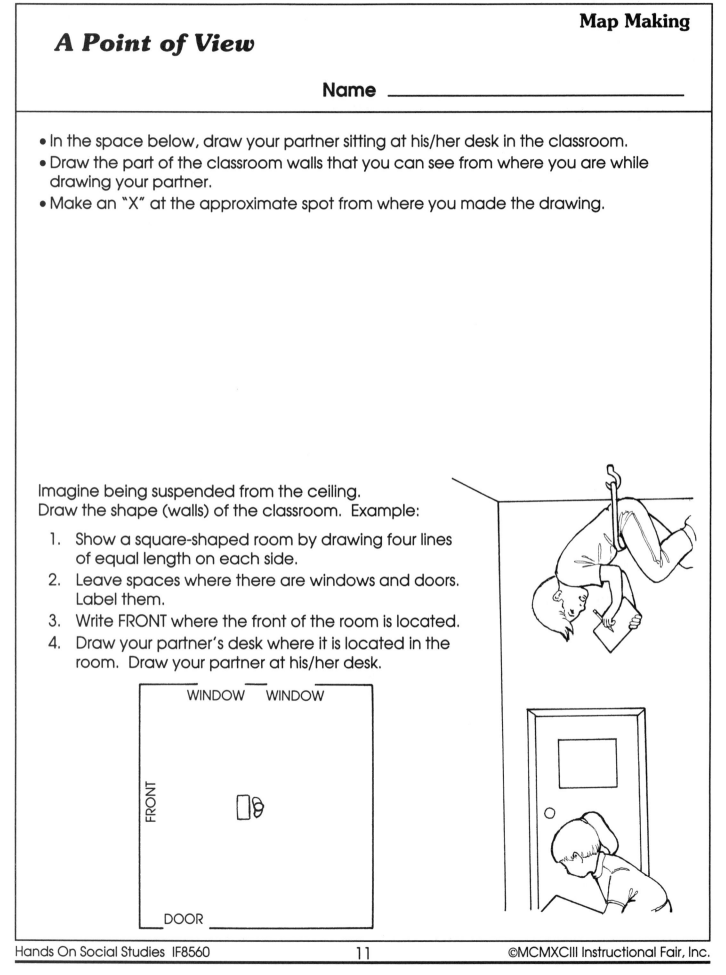

WINDOW   WINDOW

FRONT

DOOR

Map Making

Directions by Degrees

Concepts

- There are 360° in a circle and on a compass face.
- There are four primary directions with points in between.
- The magnetic needle on a compass always points toward the north magnetic pole.

Objectives

- To develop skills using a compass
- To be able to locate north with a compass
- To follow oral and written directions

Materials

overhead projector, magnetic compasses

Vocabulary

degree, 360°, cardinal directions, orient, compass

Preparation

Make 3" x 12" signs with the cardinal directions and their degrees on them.

Background Information

The dial or face of a compass usually is divided into 360 equal parts called degrees. Each degree points to a specific direction, but only the primary, or cardinal, directions - north, east, south and west - are on the compass face at 0°, 90°, 180°, and 270° respectively.

The needle on a magnetic compass always points north because it is a magnet and is attracted to Earth's north magnetic pole. If, when using a compass, one orients himself to the north, a person will be able to know in which direction to travel by turning a specific number of degrees from north.

Teaching Suggestions

- Hold a compass in your hand. At the same time, use an overhead projector to show the compass diagram to the class. Point out the compass parts on the diagram and on the actual compass. Tell students that each line on the dial represents 10°. Write 10 on the board. Point out the degree symbol (°). Explain that a circle is made up of 360°. Count the marks on the dial by tens together. NOTE: Compass faces vary. Adjust your explanation accordingly.

- Ask students if they know for what purposes compasses are used (to determine directions, find one's way, orient one's self using a map, etc.).

- Ask students if they know positively in which direction north is. Let all students who think they know to point in this direction. You might place students' names in the direction in which they pointed to see who was the most correct.

- Explain to students that north may vary a little because of interference from steel or other metal objects in the building's structure.

- If you have enough compasses, give one to every student. Otherwise have students work in small groups on the projects below.

1. Have students put their compass on a desk. First, have them turn the dial so that N, the Orienting Arrow and Direction of Travel Arrow line up as shown on the board. Walk around assisting students that need it and checking everyone. Next, tell students to turn the entire compass, including the Base Plate, until the red needle falls in line with N, the Orienting

Arrow and the Direction of Travel Arrow. (Assist and check again). When all four items are in line, explain that this is north.

2. Distribute page 13, *Directions by Degrees*. Students should complete the page. You know your class. Let them complete it independently if they are able to. After students have finished, put the direction signs (See Preparation.) up in their correct positions around the room. Keep them up all year.

3. Have students stand with compasses in hand facing what they now know as north. Tell students to hold the compasses at waist level with the Direction of Travel Arrow pointing in the same direction they are. Have them turn the dial so that N, the Orienting Arrow, and the red arrow are all pointing north, too. Have students continue to hold the compasses in this position but have them turn their entire bodies to face the east sign. Have them look at the faces on their compasses and tell what happened to them. (The Direction of Travel Arrow, N and the Orienting Arrow should have turned with them. The red arrow should have stayed where it was pointing before, to the north.) Tell them they just turned 90°. Explain to your students that when they make turns using a compass, they should always turn right from the north position. Turning by degrees is more precise than turning according to directions. Take students back to their original position (all arrows, N and their bodies facing north). Have them make several turns by degrees to the right, always from this position. (Turn 58°, 145°, 290°, etc.)

Map Making

Directions By Degrees

Name _____

Look at the diagram of the compass. Follow the directions below in order using a compass.

1. Set the compass so N (North Sign) is in line with the Direction of Travel Arrow.
2. Put the center of the compass over the dot below.
3. Keep N and Direction of Travel Arrow together. Turn the entire compass, including the Base Plate, so that N, the Direction of Travel Arrow, the red arrow, (Magnetic Arrow) and the Orienting Arrow are all pointing in the same direction.
4. Write 0° (zero degrees) on this paper at the edge of the Base Plate across from the Direction of Travel Arrow.
5. Look opposite the red arrow. The white arrow is pointing to S and/or 180°. Write 180° on this paper at the edge of the Base Plate opposite the white arrow.
6. Find 90°. It is where the E is. Write 90° on this paper at the edge of the Base Plate opposite E.
7. Find 270°. It is where the W is. Write 270° on this paper at the edge of the Base Plate opposite W.
8. Write 360° above 0°. 360° and 0° are the same.
9. Put the compass aside. Write NORTH next to 0° or 360°, EAST next to 90°, SOUTH next to 180° and WEST next to 270°.
10. Put the compass back in the same position as in #3.
11. Write 45° on the paper beside where you see it.
12. Write 135° on the paper beside where you see it.
13. Write 225° on the paper beside where you see it.
14. Write 315° on the paper beside where you see it.
15. Write NORTHEAST next to 45°, SOUTHEAST next to 135°, SOUTHWEST next to 225° and NORTHWEST next to 315°.

NORTH, SOUTH, EAST and WEST are the cardinal directions. NORTHEAST, SOUTHEAST, SOUTHWEST and NORTHWEST are the intercardinal directions.

DIRECTION OF TRAVEL ARROW
NORTH SIGN
ORIENTING ARROW
CENTER
MAGNETIC ARROW
DIAL
BASE PLATE

Map Making

Make a Map

Concepts

- Compasses determine directions.
- A compass bearing is calculated by the number of degrees something is from north.
- A protractor is used to record a bearing on a map.
- Every map has a scale of miles to calculate distance.

Objectives

- To develop skills using a compass
- To learn how to use a protractor
- To learn how to calculate distance on a map
- To learn how to make a map
- To learn how to follow directions

Materials

rulers, protractors, compasses, pencils with erasers, black felt-tip pens, masking tape, 16" - 18" sheets of paper (or larger)

Vocabulary

protractor, scale, map symbols, pace, bearing, key

Preparation

Cut paper into 16" - 18" squares. Obtain several types of maps: road, state, country and world, city plans, etc.

Background Information

Maps have been used for thousands of years to indicate routes, land formations, hunting grounds, amounts of rainfall in different areas, etc. Ancient maps were not accurate by today's standards, and they had empty spaces that were filled with drawings. As more information about the world was gained from the records of explorers and other travelers, maps increased in accuracy although a full view of the world was impossible from land or sea. With the capability of aerial photography today, it became possible to view the entire world and thus produce accurate maps.

Teaching Suggestions

- This lesson should be divided into at least three parts. Teach students about the protractor one day, the scale another and actual map making another.

- Show students several maps. Have them tell where north is on each one. Ask what conclusion they can draw about where north is on most maps. Establish where east, south and west are located. Explain that when students make their maps, they will still use a compass to find directions and determine degrees. But when they put their maps on paper, they will use a protractor. Teach students about protractors if they are not familiar with them by doing steps A-G below.

A. Show students a protractor. Ask what part of a circle a protractor is. Then ask how many degrees that is. Point out the degree marks on it. Count them aloud together by tens.

B. Using a ruler, demonstrate how a protractor is used. Draw a vertical line on the board. Write NORTH direction above the line. Tell students it is called the "north line". Put a dot just below the line.

C. Explain to students that usually, the number of degrees an object (such as a tree) is from north is first measured by a compass. Tell them that for the next part of the lesson, you will be presenting some degrees and objects although they were previously measured and recorded. Example: Tell students the first object (a bicycle) was 42° from north. Show this location on a map (bulletin board).

D. Show them how to set the middle of the protractor along north line. Point out 0° at the top and 180° at the bottom of the protractor. Have a student point to 42°. Mark it with a dot at the edge of the protractor.

E. Remove the protractor and draw a line from the dot at the bottom of the north line to the dot that shows 42°.

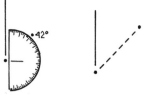

F. Demonstrate how to mark degrees on a map several more times before allowing students to use protractors. Include bearings more than 180°. (Place protractor on other side of north line.)

G. Give students protractors, rulers, pencils and paper. Tell them first to draw a dot in the middle of their paper. Then, tell them to draw a north line from the dot to the top. Give students bearings of the paper. Have them practice drawing lines to show degrees from north. Assist and check until students understand this concept.

14

Map Making

Make a Map continued

• Once students understand how to record direction, they must find distance. Tell students that actual distances between points are impossible to show on a map. You will show them how to reduce those distances to fit on a map.

A. Begin by showing students several maps. Point out the map scales. Tell student that scales are ratios between actual distances and measurements that are equal to the actual distances. Examine the scales together. Let students determine the ratios of different scales.

B. Draw a north line with a dot below it on the board. Draw several bearing lines away from north. Tell students to assume that the bearing lines point in the direction of several objects that have been measured with a compass and protractor.

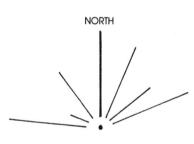

NORTH

C. Remind students how several of the maps they looked at used a ratio of inches to miles (ie: 1" equals 100 miles). Tell them that the ratio on the maps they make will be one inch to every four steps. Draw a line one inch long. Put a line at either end. Above it, write 1" = 4 steps. Explain that this is how the scale will look on your map.

D. Use the diagram above (B)

to demonstrate scale. Make up the number of steps it would take to reach the end of each line (ie: 8, 18, 13, 32, etc.). Calculate the steps to figure out how many inches each line should be. Measure and draw the inches each line should be. Erase any excess if some of the lines on diagram B are too long. Keep practicing this concept until it is understood.

• Remind students that actual objects like trees, furniture, roads, etc. are not shown on a map as such. Rather, a representation or symbol is used for these objects. Let students suggest how they might show a building, bush, playground equipment, etc. Draw some symbols at the end of each line in D. Tell students that the objects the symbols represent on a map are shown on the map key. The scale is also part of the key.

• When you feel the students are ready to make a map, divide them into pairs. Have a student(s) who understands the methods to be used, work with one who is less sure.

• Distribute pages 16 and 17, *Make a Map*. Go over it with the class before letting pairs proceed.

• Assign an area to each pair. Each area should be small and well-defined (ie: classroom, part of classroom, playground equipment area, nurse's office, etc.). Some pairs may do the same areas.

• When the maps are finished, suggest that each pair exchange its map with another pair's map. Let pairs check each other's maps.

• Follow-up Activities:

1. Take one or more of the maps that have been made. Make multiple copies. Make up a scavenger hunt. Write the first direction. Example: "Begin at (name place). Take 16 steps at 63. Hidden at this destination will be the next clue." The student should read the clue and put it back for the next person before doing what the clue says. Continue in this manner until the last message indicates the end of the hunt.

2. Make a map of a nearby park, playground, etc. Make multiple copies. Give students a set of directions that will tell them where to begin, how far to move in a specific direction and what to mark on the map before following the next instruction. This is similar to #1 except the map is made by you, all information is given at one time on an instruction sheet, and students mark the map at each destination instead of finding notes.

3. Obtain a map of a local park, sanctuary, plant, reservation, etc. Read the map of the area with the class. Let students point out some features on the map. Take the class to the location. Have students check some of the features shown on the map using their compasses.

4. Look at some early maps. Compare them to maps of today.

Notes/Ideas for Next Time

Write on another sheet of paper.

Make a Map

Name _____

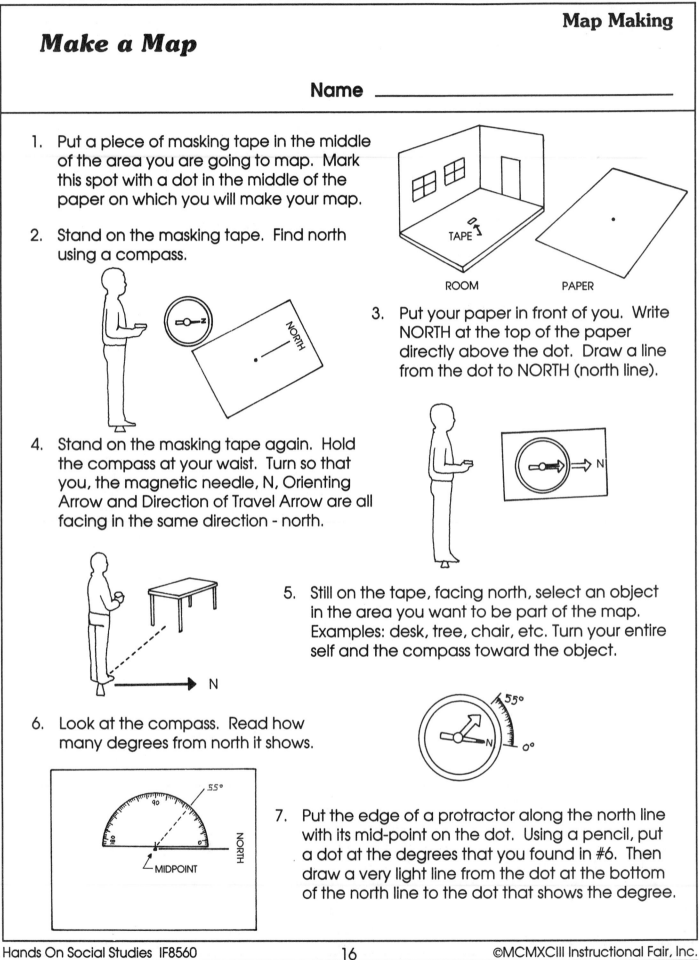

1. Put a piece of masking tape in the middle of the area you are going to map. Mark this spot with a dot in the middle of the paper on which you will make your map.

2. Stand on the masking tape. Find north using a compass.

3. Put your paper in front of you. Write NORTH at the top of the paper directly above the dot. Draw a line from the dot to NORTH (north line).

4. Stand on the masking tape again. Hold the compass at your waist. Turn so that you, the magnetic needle, N, Orienting Arrow and Direction of Travel Arrow are all facing in the same direction - north.

5. Still on the tape, facing north, select an object in the area you want to be part of the map. Examples: desk, tree, chair, etc. Turn your entire self and the compass toward the object.

6. Look at the compass. Read how many degrees from north it shows.

7. Put the edge of a protractor along the north line with its mid-point on the dot. Using a pencil, put a dot at the degrees that you found in #6. Then draw a very light line from the dot at the bottom of the north line to the dot that shows the degree.

Map Making

Make a Map continued

Name _____

8. Now that you know the direction, show how far the object is from the masking tape. Step from the tape to the object. Count your steps.

9. Make a scale in the lower left corner of the map. Let one inch equal four of your steps. Write **Scale** . Below it, write 1" = 4 steps. Under it, draw a one-inch line with a small vertical line at either end.

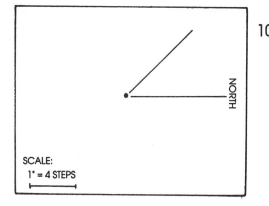

SCALE:
1" = 4 STEPS

10. With a pencil, draw a line to scale over the one you drew in #7 that represents the number of steps taken to the object. Remember to draw the line lightly because it will be erased at the end of the worksheet. Draw the line from the dot under the north line in the direction (number of degrees from north) of the object. The example is 2" which represents 8 steps.

11. Objects or features on a map are represented by symbols. What each symbol represents is shown on the map's KEY. Write **KEY** about an inch above Scale: . As you decide what objects will be on your map and what the symbol for each will be, fill in the key. An example is shown to the left.

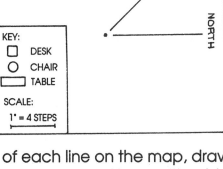

KEY:
☐ DESK
○ CHAIR
▭ TABLE
SCALE:
1" = 4 STEPS

12. At the end of each line on the map, draw the symbol for the object. Do it with a black felt-tip pen.

13. Continue steps 4 through 12 for all objects to be included on the map.

14. When all the objects have been placed in position on the map, erase the pencil lines. Then you will have a map.

KEY:
☐ DESK
○ CHAIR
▭ TABLE
SCALE:
1" = 4 STEPS

17

Map Making

Land Formations

Concepts

- Elevation is measured from sea level.
- Sea level is zero elevation.
- Different land formations make up the land surface of Earth.
- The steeper a land formation's slope, the closer together its contour lines on a topographical map are (and vice versa).

Objectives

- To recognize different land formations
- To develop ability to draw conclusions from contour lines on a map
- To develop ability to read topographical maps

Materials

overhead projector, chalk (yellow, yellow-green, green, tan, brown, red), topographical maps, other materials to be found with the last project under Teaching Suggestions

Preparation

Obtain topographical maps. If you live near a major city, try a map or sporting goods store. If not available where you live, write:

U.S. Geological Survey Map Distribution
P.O. Box 25286
Denver, CO 80225

Ask for Topo Index and Catalog. It will give a listing by state of dealers who sell topo maps.

Background Information

Sometimes it is important to know the elevation of the Earth's surface. Pilots want to fly high enough to avoid mountain peaks. Hikers want to know the terrain so they plan a route that is not impossible. Road builders want to construct a highway where the Earth's surface will require the least amount of moving. A topographic map gives the best information about the surface of the Earth. It includes elevation and can include manmade and natural physical features.

Elevation is shown on a map with contour lines. If the elevation of an area is at sea level, it has no contour lines. Sea level is zero elevation. One contour line is the same distance from sea level all the way around. The next line, though higher, is the same distance around. As a formation narrows toward the top, the line covers less area. The lines are not always equal distances apart. The gentler an incline, the further apart the lines.

Teaching Suggestions

- Use an overhead projector to show the drawings below to the class.

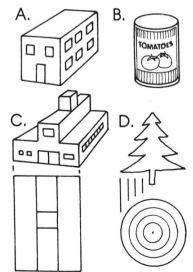

A.   B.

C.   D.

Ask students to describe each picture as they see it (not what it is, but how it looks - its shape). Then ask students what they would see if they were to hang glide above each drawing and could only see it from the top. Have them draw it. Lead them into seeing different levels in C and D and how they might show them. Explain that a picture gives an idea of an object's height and what it looks like on two sides. An object's height and all of its sides and levels may be seen from a position above the object.

- Show students topographical maps. Point out the contour lines. Explain that they show elevation. Ask students when they think knowledge of elevation might be useful.

- Draw contour lines on the board - something like the ones shown below. Each line is the same distance above sea level. The number on each contour line tells the elevation of the land at that point. The height shown by each line may not be in equal intervals because the position of one line next to another tells the steepness of the land at that point. When the incline is steep, the contour lines are closer together. Ask a student to point to the steepest part in the drawing. (Clarification: Contour lines show the up and down of Earth's surface. The distance between two points across the map is shown according to the scale.

N

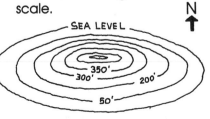

SEA LEVEL

350'
300'   200'

50'

18

Land Formations continued

Map Making

- Draw two side views of the hill shown on page 18. Ask students which is the east-west view and which is the north-south. Ask how they can tell.

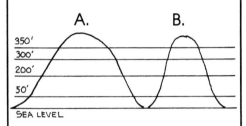

- Elevation may also be shown with color. Have students color all three figures on the board as directed so they can see how a picture or a topographical map shows the same thing. Color as follows: sea level = green, sea level to 50' = yellow-green, 50 to 200' = yellow, 200 to 300' = blue, 300 to 350' = brown, above 350' = red.

- Use an overhead projector to show the topographical maps shown below. Tell students these maps show two different land formations. Ask what they can conclude from studying them and how they came to their conclusion. Ask students to draw a picture (side view) of how they visualize A and B. Continue in this manner (topo map, side view picture) until students understand the concept. Ask what they think an area on a map looks like if there are no contour lines.

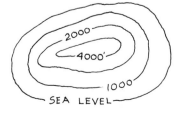

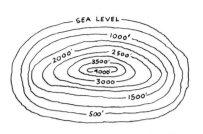

- Select formations on Earth listed below that you want your students to know. Write their names on the board. Instruct your students to do one or more of the suggestions listed below: archipelago, cliff, headland, mesa, plateau, atoll, coastline, hill, mountain, riverbed, badlands, crevasse, island, mountain range, sea, bay, continent, isthmus, palisade, strait, butte, delta, key, peak, summit, canyon, dune, knoll, peninsula, valley, cave, fjord, lake, pinnacle, volcano

Suggestions:

1. Fold a piece of paper into fourths and open it up.

Select four land formations. Draw a picture of each one in one of the sections formed on the paper. Write the name of each formation.

2. Write definitions for a (specified) number of land formations.

3. Find examples of different land formations (canyon - Grand Canyon, sea - Caspian, etc.). Write a report about a specific land formation.

4. Distribute page 20, *Land Formations.* After going over it with students, have them complete it on their own.

5. Make Your State Art Project

Materials Needed- opaque projector, thin cardboard, pencils, scissors, newspaper, papier-mâché, paints, brushes

Find a good outline of your state. Enlarge it using an opaque projector. Cut the outline out. Trace around it on a piece of cardboard. Cut the cardboard outline out. Make a cardboard outline for each group of 3-5 students.

Have each group make a "base land" out of papier-mâché by laying one coat over the cardboard. While it is drying, instruct students to learn all they can about the geography of their state.

When they have completed their research, tell them to draw or write the names of the state's geographic features on the "base land" approximately where they are located.

Have them use papier-mâché to add the geographic formations that are elevated by building up hills, etc. Let them dry.

When the papier-mâché is dry, instruct students to paint the state and to paint in the lakes, rivers, etc.

Notes/Ideas for Next Time

_____
_____
_____
_____
_____
_____
_____

Map Making

Land Formations

Name _____

Select three of the land formations listed below. Draw each one following the directions after them.

| MESA   MOUNTAIN RANGE   ISLAND   BUTTE   PLATEAU   HILL |

Draw a topographic view and a picture of each formation. Space the contour lines to show each formation's shape. Write each line's elevation. Your topographic map will determine each formation's shape in its picture.

Land Formation 1

Topographical Map   Picture

Land Formation 2

Topographical Map   Picture

Land Formation 3

Topographical Map   Picture

20

Law and Order

The Federal and State Court Systems

Concepts

- The authority of federal courts is derived from the United States Constitution and federal laws.
- State courts obtain their authority from each state's constitution and state laws.
- The U.S. Supreme Court is the highest court in the land.
- All courts are presided over by a judge.
- Courts try cases and administer the law.
- A case is either a criminal or civil matter.

Objectives

- To be aware of federal and state courts, their similarities and differences, their jurisdictions and who presides over them
- To be able to distinguish between criminal and civil matters

Vocabulary

circuit court (state), district court (federal), appellate court, criminal matter, civil matter, jurisdiction, preside, justice, decision

Preparation

- Make enough copies of Article II, Section 2 of the U.S. Constitution for the class.
- Make enough copies of Article III, Sections 1 and 2 of the U.S. Constitution for the class.
- Make enough copies of the part of your state's constitution that pertains to its court system for the class.
- Make enough copies of the diagram on page 24 for the class.

Background Information

There are courts at both the federal and state levels. There are several divisions in both systems. Not all states have courts of appeals. However, all states have a high court though it may not necessarily be called a "supreme court". Courts resolve conflicts between individuals, organizations, companies, government or any combination of the aforementioned. Federal courts handle cases involving the Constitution and federal laws. They also handle cases when the United States government is one of the parties involved. State courts handle cases that fall under state law or jurisdiction.

The court system outlined in the U.S. Constitution provides for the right to a fair trial from the lowest court to the highest. If an unsatisfactory decision is handed down, an appeal may be made to a higher court. If that court's judgment is not satisfactory, a request for a hearing by an even higher court may be made. The possibility of moving through a state court system to the U.S. Supreme Court exists because of how the U.S. Constitution was written 200 years ago.

Teaching Suggestions

- Present the next two activities at separate times.

  1) Distribute Article II, Section 2 and Article III, Sections 1 and 2 of the U.S. Constitution to the class. Read them together making interpretations where necessary. Then ask students the following questions:

  -How did the Supreme Court get started?
  -Does the Constitution say how many justices should be on it?
  -Who appoints the justices?
  -What else must be done before the appointed justice is allowed to sit on the Supreme Court?
  -What are some of the duties of the Supreme Court?
  -Under what branch (department) of the U.S. government does the Supreme Court fall?

  2) Distribute to the class the part of your state's constitution that pertains to its court system. Read this with the class making interpretations where necessary. Then ask students the following questions:

  -Name the courts (lower, trial, appeal, etc.) in the state.
  -How do judges in the state get their jobs?
  -Do all the state courts deal with civil and criminal cases, or do separate courts handle such cases? Explain.
  -How many high courts (or supreme courts) are there in the state? Where are they? How many district courts and circuit courts are there?

- Make copies of the diagram of *The Federal and State Court Systems* (page 24) for every student. Distribute them. Discuss the flow of the courts and compare the federal and state systems. (When a state does not have an appellate court, a second case hearing goes to the next court above.)

The Federal and State Court Systems continued

Law and Order

- Write the terms **Criminal** and **Civil** on the board. Ask students if their state's courts have separate courts for each matter or if all courts hear both. If they have separate courts, make a diagram depicting which types of cases are heard by which courts.
- Suggest some types of cases that might come before the state courts: assault, divorce, property line settlement, robbery, car accident, etc. Ask students to tell under which category, criminal or civil, they each would be.
- Have students list the state's specialized or lower courts on their diagrams. Do this with the students as a result of reading part of the state constitution.
- Other Activities:

  1. Have students write the names of the justices of the U.S. Supreme Court. Have them write a biography about one of the justices.

  2. Have your students bring newspaper articles dealing with federal and state courts to share them. If there are situations the students comprehend, ask them for their opinions and what they think the outcome should (or might) be.

  3. Invite a judge or other court personnel to visit with your class.

  4. Take your class on a field trip to visit a courtroom.

Opening Statement and Closing Argument

Law and Order

Concepts

- There are always two sides in a trial.
- A judge, attorneys for both sides, a court reporter and a clerk are always present in a courtroom for a trial.
- A person is entitled to a jury in all criminal cases.
- Juries listen to evidence and examine the facts and decide if they are true or not.

Objectives

- To become knowledgeable about a courtroom
- To understand courtroom proceedings
- To develop drawing-conclusion skills
- To develop interpretation skills
- To develop stating-the-main-idea skills

Vocabulary

Criminal Procedure: acquittal, alleged, arraignment, conviction, indictment, sentence

Courtroom Terminology: adversary, appeal, bench, closing argument, cross-examination, deliberate, direct examination, evidence, oath, opening statement, suit, summons, testimony, verdict

Courtroom Personalities: attorney, bailiff, clerk, court reporter, defendant, foreman, grand jury, judge, jury, plaintiff, prosecutor, process server, witness

Preparation

- Look for, and save, news articles about courtroom proceedings.
- Make enough copies of Constitutional Amendments V, VI, VII, and VIII for the class.

Background Information

Juries are representatives of the people. They check to see that the law is fair and that the court alone does not have too much power. The U.S. Constitution, and most state constitutions, mention a right to trial by jury, although there are some trials where juries are never used. (Divorce and bankruptcy are two such types in which a jury is not used.) Juries must be requested by the defendant in cases where they are allowed. Otherwise, a judge alone will hear the case.

Teaching Suggestions

- Carry out four activities listed at separate times.

  1) Distribute copies of the U.S. Constitution's Amendments V, VI, VII and VIII. Read them together, when necessary. Ask students what these amendments deal with and what some of the laws are for getting a fair trial.

  2) Review with your class what criminal cases are. Discuss definitions for the vocabulary words under Criminal Procedure. Ask the following questions:

  -When is a person an alleged criminal?

Opening Statement and Closing Argument continued

Law and Order

-What happens to a person after an acquittal? indictment? conviction?

-What is the purpose of an arraignment?

3) Define the positions of the people listed under Courtroom Personalities who might be in a courtroom. Look at news articles for mention of them.

4) Discuss the words listed under Courtroom Terminology and when and how they fit into courtroom procedure.

• Discuss more about opening statements and closing arguments if you feel it is necessary before distributing page 25, *Opening Statements and Closing Arguments.* Make sure that students understand that an opening statement should declare what the attorney intends to prove and that a closing argument should enumerate the reasons for a decision in favor of the attorney's client. There are four possible activities on the worksheets. They may be done in one of the following ways: together at four different times, individually at four different times, or divide the class into four groups and make one group responsible for one side of each case. The latter may be done as a group activity or individually. When the students have completed the worksheets, have some of them on opposing sides present their arguments to a jury. Have the jury deliberate after each pair's presentation and come up with a verdict. Do this two or three times so everyone has a chance to be on a jury.

• Optional: Divide students into small groups. Have them work together to write a short play, set in a courtroom, using one of the situations from the worksheets as the subject. Let them choose the ones they will use from the opening statements and closing arguments already written. This will help structure the play. Included in the play must be the defendant, the plaintiff, their attorneys, the judge, the bailiff, the court reporter and witnesses. Have students present the play. Students who are not in it may act as the jury.

• Ask students if they know anyone who has served on a jury. If they do, perhaps they could invite that person to speak to the class about the experience.

• Have students look for current articles about trials. Have them bring them to share with the group. Put them up on a small bulletin board entitled: FROM THE BENCH.

• Law schools often hold mock trials. If you live near a university that has a law school, make arrangements for your class to sit in on a mock trial.

• Visit a courtroom in the courthouse near you. If there is a trial in session, perhaps your class could sit in the courtroom to see the legal system at work. Use your discretion about this activity.

• Some of the states' courts do not allow photographers into their courtrooms during trials, but they will allow artists to sketch the proceedings. Have your students sketch a trial.

Notes/Ideas for Next Time

_____
_____
_____
_____
_____
_____
_____
_____
_____
_____
_____
_____
_____
_____
_____
_____
_____
_____
_____
_____
_____
_____
_____
_____
_____
_____
_____
_____
_____
_____
_____
_____

Law and Order

The Federal and State Court Systems

Name _____

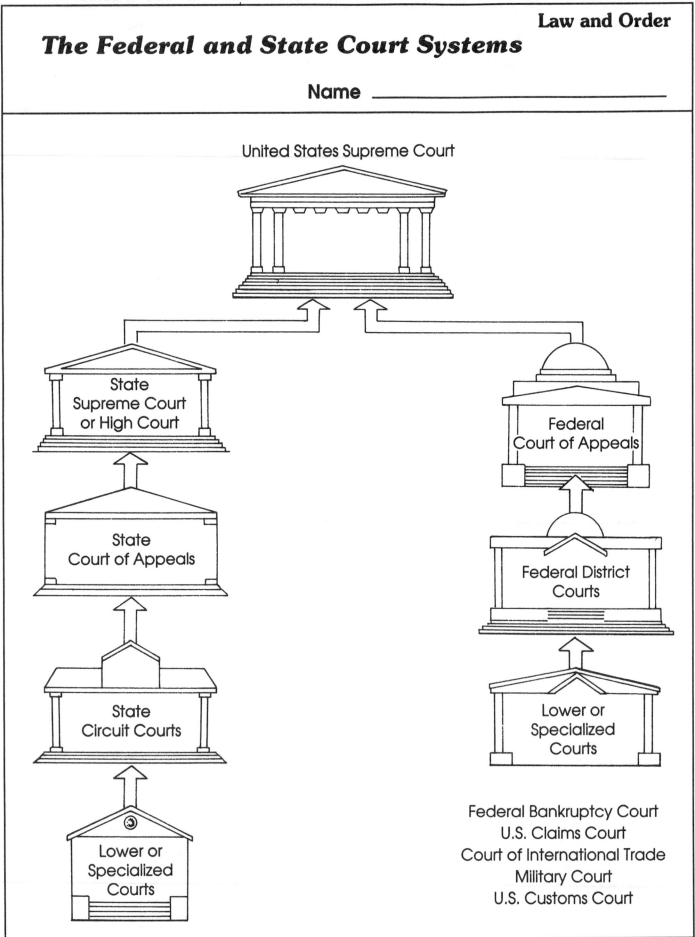

United States Supreme Court

State Supreme Court or High Court

Federal Court of Appeals

State Court of Appeals

Federal District Courts

State Circuit Courts

Lower or Specialized Courts

Lower or Specialized Courts

Federal Bankruptcy Court
U.S. Claims Court
Court of International Trade
Military Court
U.S. Customs Court

24

Opening Statement and Closing Argument

Name _____

Read the summary of the case below. Then, fill in the names of the defendant and plaintiff and for which one you will write an opening statement:

Defendant: _____   Plaintiff: _____

For which one will you write an opening statement? _____

Hopetown has a leash law. It says, "All dogs must be penned in their owner's yard or on a leash whenever they are not penned."

On June 15, 1992, a delivery man left the gate to the Smyth's yard open. The Smyth's dog took the opportunity to "escape". Some children were playing baseball in the street outside the gate. Just as the dog came out of its yard, the ball rolled away from the players. The dog snatched the ball up in its mouth and ran into its yard. The ball belonged to Jim Thomas. He wanted his ball, so he ran after the dog. When Jim caught the dog by its tail and reached for the ball in its mouth, the dog dropped the ball, but bit Jim. Jim had to have 22 stitches in his arm. Jim is suing the Smyths for damages.

_____
_____
_____
_____
_____
_____
_____
_____

Now, write a closing argument for the same person for whom you wrote an opening statement.

_____
_____
_____
_____
_____
_____
_____
_____

Opening Statement and Closing Argument continued

Name _____

Read the summary of the case below. Then, fill in the names of the defendant and plaintiff and for which one you will write an opening statement:

Defendant: _____   Plaintiff: _____

For which one will you write an opening statement? _____

For the past twenty years, Mrs. Casswell had walked the three blocks from the bus stop to her house after work every day at approximately 5:15 p.m. She could find the way home with her eyes closed because she was so familiar with the route. On April 12th last year when she was passing the Newhalls' house, she noticed they were planting some new shrubbery. Mrs. Casswell was so interested in the project that she did not see the hose stretched across the walk. She tripped over it and fell. The Newhalls called an ambulance to take her to the hospital. Mrs. Casswell had broken her hip. She stayed in the hospital for almost a month and then had to stay at home for another three months during her recovery. Mrs. Casswell sued the Newhalls for her medical expenses and the lost wages by not being able to work.

_____
_____
_____
_____
_____
_____
_____

Now, write a closing argument for the same person for whom you wrote an opening statement.

_____
_____
_____
_____
_____
_____
_____
_____

 ©MCMXCIII Instructional Fair, Inc.

Colonial Life

Reading and Writing in Colonial America

Concepts

- The colonial period in America was from 1607 until 1775.
- Settlers to the New World sought a better life for economic and religious reasons.
- The settlers came from different backgrounds.
- The settlers overcame the many obstacles by which they were confronted and founded a new nation.

Objectives

- To understand reasons why early settlers came to the New World
- To realize the New World's settlers came from different places and brought with them different beliefs and customs
- To develop some understanding of what life was like during the colonial period
- To express briefly something about colonial life

Vocabulary

Puritan, Quaker, Huguenot, Pilgrim, indentured servant, charter, colony, proprietor

Background Information

The colonial period in America began in 1607 with the founding of Jamestown and ended in 1775 with the start of the Revolutionary War. The majority of colonists were English, but settlers came from almost every Western European country too. Although their backgrounds and customs were different, they all came to America because they were unhappy with their lives in the Old World and hoped for better ones in a new one.

The new settlers knew settling in the New World would not be easy, but they were ready to face the hardships in return for political and religious freedom and economic opportunity. With the arrival of more and more settlers and natural growth, America's population increased to about one and a half million people during the colonial period.

Teaching Suggestions

- Discuss several of the following details or features about colonial life.
  -Ask students what sort of people they believe the early settlers had to be to undertake the venture they did. (adventurous, determined, strong, etc.)
  -Ask what one family might have packed if they could bring just one trunk, or if they could bring one other item, what it might have been.
  -Ask what kind of shelter these early settlers might have built for immediate use after landing in the New World. Have students consider the materials available and whether the colonists thought about the environment.
  -Discuss how the colonists may have handled everyday situations that we take for granted such as obtaining food, keeping food fresh, putting out fires, communicating with the closest neighbor five miles away, etc.
  -Discuss how the settlers cooperated in work and play.
  -Ask what chores the children probably had to do.
- Ask students how the settlers' lives changed from the time they arrived in 1607 until the end of the colonial period in 1775. (ie: clothes, food, hardships, etc.) Discuss why the changes occurred.
- Show your students copies of early primers and the horn book. Have them compare books from back then to books available now.
- Ask students why they think there were not too many books for educational purposes in the beginning. Explain that that is why proverbs (such as those in "Poor Richard's Almanac") and original verses with religious themes or about the King made up some of the early lessons in which the colonial students learned to read and write. Read some proverbs from "Poor Richard's Almanac" to the students. Discuss their relevancy today.
- Distribute page 28, *Reading and Writing in Colonial America*. When it is completed, let students share their original verses before putting their work up on a bulletin board.
- Additional Activities:
  1. Ask your school or community librarian to help you put together a library of books about life in colonial America. Set up a resource area in your room. Let students use it for assigned work or recreational browsing.
  2. Instruct students to a) read a book or article from the class library and write a report, b) find and copy a recipe from colonial times (you could make a cookbook), c) research colonial dress and either draw or make and wear one of the styles of the time, d) write a biography about an early colonist.
  3. Divide the class into groups. Assign each group a specific event (voyage to the New World, the sighting of land, building a first home, etc.). Tell the group to write a short vignette about it and to perform it.
  4. Tell students to write a letter to someone in the Old World and tell about their life in the new one. Tell students to draw a picture to show the person what their new home looks like.
  5. Have students write a paragraph of what they might say if they were the town crier. Have them perform their message.
  6. Have a "neighbor party" in Colonial America. Have students dress in colonial costume. Cook and serve some of the recipes the students copied (#2b).

27

Colonial Life

Reading and Writing in Colonial America

Name _____

Copy the proverbs below taken from "Poor Richard's Almanac" in your best handwriting. Then, interpret them through illustrations.

Lost time is never found again.

_____

_____

_____

Don't throw stones at your neighbors, if you live in a glass house.

_____

_____

_____

Early to bed and early to rise, makes a man healthy, wealthy and wise.

_____

_____

_____

_____

Write a two-line verse that could have been written by a student in colonial times that tells something about his/her life then. Illustrate your poem in the box.

_____

_____

_____

_____

Getting the Work Done

Colonial Life

Concepts

- There was little time for recreation in colonial times.
- Neighbors helped neighbors and had fun doing it.

Objectives

- To learn about cooperation
- To develop writing conversation skills
- To expand an introductory statement or main idea

Materials

optional: See suggestions for follow-up activities.

Vocabulary

monologue, conversation, barn-raising, bee
optional: afghan, sampler, embroidery, applique (follow-up activities)

Preparation

- Obtain pictures that show people involved in activities during colonial times. Look in art books, at art postcards and reproductions and in texts or encyclopedias.
- If possible, borrow an old quilt (or a copy).
- Teach students how to write dialogue.

Background Information

The colonists did not have much time for recreation. Therefore, they made their work fun. Sometimes they made a party out of work. A quilting bee was one way women turned a tiresome task into a pleasurable one, and a barn-raising was a way the men made hard work enjoyable.

Teaching Suggestions

- Ask students what they think the colonists did for fun. Explain that they did not have much time for recreation, so they made their work fun. If a neighbor needed a barn, the men and boys would get together and build it in a day that ended with games, food and conversation. A housewife in need of a quilt would invite several women or young ladies to a quilting bee where they would sit around a quilting frame and stitch the layers of a quilt together and exchange news and gossip.
- Show students pictures of the colonists in recreational activities. Talk about them.
- Distribute page 30, *Getting the Work Done* to the girls and page 31 to the boys. They may be done individually or in small groups. You may want to assign each small group to a different conversation. Whichever way you choose, explain how the page is to be done. Explain that they may have to do some research to make a conversation authentic.
- When students are finished with worksheets, share them with the class. Have students act them out in conversation form.
- Follow-up Activities:
  1. Make one of the things listed below that the settlers made. Directions are not given because there are many craft books available that contain how-to instructions.
  Group Crafts -
  A. Patchwork Quilt - Have students make a real quilt or give each student a piece of graph paper on which to design a square. Put the squares together and hang in the classroom.
  B. Afghan - Have each student knit a square or two. Sew them together. Give it to a needy person.
  Individual Activities - sampler, embroidery, applique, candles
  2. Tell students that some of the games the colonial children played, and the contests they held, are the same as some of the ones they participate in today (ie: marbles, spelling bees, leapfrog, blindman's bluff, hopscotch, kite flying). Take time to play some of them. Ask students why they think colonial children did not play football, baseball, lacrosse, etc.

Notes/Ideas for Next Time

_____
_____
_____
_____
_____
_____
_____
_____
_____
_____
_____
_____
_____
_____

Colonial Life

Getting the Work Done

Name _____

Write a monologue or a conversation that could have taken place after each of the opening remarks below made by women at a quilting bee.

Martha Brown said, "My cousin wrote from England that he will be sailing for the New World next month."

_____

_____

_____

_____

_____

Priscilla Jones reported, "After dinner last night, we heard something outside that made us run to the window." _____

_____

_____

_____

_____

_____

Jane Smith asked, "Does anyone want to order some material from England? I am going to ask my friend to bring me three yards of calico when she comes here."

_____

_____

_____

_____

_____

Mary Thomas said, "My daughter is going to be ten years old tomorrow." _____

_____

_____

_____

_____

 ©MCMXCIII Instructional Fair, Inc.

Colonial Life

Getting the Work Done continued

Name _____

Write a monologue or a conversation that could have taken place after each of the opening remarks below made by men during the social hour that followed the barn raising.

Benjamin Brown said, "I have more deer than ever before. They are eating my shrubs."

_____
_____
_____
_____
_____

William Jones related, "When I went outside this morning, there were huge deer tracks below the front window." _____
_____
_____
_____
_____
_____

Roger Smith asked, "When is the school teacher arriving, and what living arrangements have been made for him?" _____
_____
_____
_____
_____

John Thomas spoke with conviction when he said, "It is time we keep more for ourselves and stop sending so much to England." _____
_____
_____
_____
_____

Social Issues

Similarities and Differences

Concepts

- Similarities and differences exist among human beings.
- Distinguishing characteristics do not make one person better than another.
- The similarities of all members of the human race are greater than the differences.
- Everyone has a right to respect and justice.
- Everyone is special.

Objectives

- To observe similarities and differences among human beings
- To realize that some traits may distinguish one person from another
- To realize the no one trait in a person makes that person better than another
- To recognize some personal traits and traits of others
- To develop comparison skills

Materials

Sets of objects and pictures (See Preparation.)

Vocabulary

trait, discrimination, prejudice, stereotype, minority group, racism

Preparation

Collect sets of pictures of objects (ie: people in different dress, a bird, butterfly, bee, penguin, rubber ball, ball of yarn, football, etc.) to be compared ahead of this activity.

Background Information

There perhaps is a tendency not to talk about unpleasant conditions, such as racism, with young people. There is often a fear that talking about it will raise feelings and accelerate actions that might otherwise not occur. However, discussing these types of situations can help students realize their existence and can aid in dealing with the varied emotions associated with them. Early openness hopefully may prevent later discrimination and prejudice.

Teaching Suggestions

- Show students different sets of objects or pictures. Ask them to tell what the similarities and differences are among the members of each set.
- Ask students what they think of the following statements:

  People over 60 are old and grouchy. Immigrants are stupid. Doberman pinschers are ferocious dogs. Girls are weak.

  Explain that statements linking all members of a certain group with a particular characteristic and creating false representation of the group are called stereotypes. Such statements are sometimes made about minority groups. Some may be complimentary. Others are not. You might ask students some of the stereotypical remarks they have heard and ask them if they believe the remarks are true.

  (Examples: Blacks are great athletes. Jews are smart. The Japanese are good mathematicians.)

- Ask students if anyone has ever experienced prejudice or discrimination. If they have, have them tell about it and how it made them feel.

- Divide students into small groups. Assign one of the situations below (or make up some you think are appropriate for your class) to each group. Instruct each group to act out the situation, to extend it with words that show discrimination or prejudice and to add an ending. The ending may show a right or wrong approach to rectify the situation. After each performance, ask for student reactions. Was the treatment fair? Why or why not? What other solutions might there have been? From the discussions, help students conclude that: a)Everyone is entitled to respect regardless of his/her traits, b)No one person or group is better than another because of personal traits, c)Not all people who belong to a group have the same traits, and conversely, all people who belong to a group have some of the same traits, and d)Get to know someone before you develop an opinion about the person.

Situations:

1. A new neighbor who happens to be (black/white/hispanic/Asian - whichever is a minority in your neighborhood) is standing on the curb watching the neighborhood children play a game.
2. The champion girl racer was not allowed to join the boy's relay team.
3. Margot wears the same clothes almost all the time because her family does not have enough money to buy her

Similarities and Differences continued

Social Issues

different outfits. However, her clothes are always very clean.

4. A Jewish student in the class cannot participate in the class overnight Friday because it is the beginning of the Sabbath.

5. A sign on the restaurant's door said, "Only people from English or French backgrounds may eat here".

6. Anyone over 65 may not live on Mulberry Street because that is too old to be a good neighbor.

7. Timothy is the only student in the class who wears glasses.

8. A boy causes his team to lose the game because he

struck out.

- Before distributing page 35, *Similarities and Differences*, talk about the meanings of the following phrases: "a chip off the old block", "like night and day", and "two peas in a pod". Distribute the worksheet and tell students to follow the page's directions. The examples may or may not be a comparison using themselves. The person they choose to compare themselves with on the second part of the page may come from a list of personalities presented by you (ie: athletes, performers, etc., admired by students) or a person they know.
- After students complete the

worksheet, have them read their examples of the phrases and ask them if they found more similarities or differences in their comparisons of themselves with other people.

- Have students make a list of "How to Treat Others Regardless of Traits". Keep it up in the room as a reminder of expected behaviors.
- Make copies of the following. Give one to each student to complete.

I am what I am,

You are what you are,

We _____

_____

Getting to Know the Newspaper

Communication

Concepts

- Front pages of different newspapers may not look alike.
- Newspapers may not look alike, but most of them contain many of the same components.
- A newspaper's copy is different every day.
- Newspapers provide information and entertainment.

Objectives

- To become familiar with newspaper terminology and content
- To locate specific information and components
- To develop skills needed to read a newspaper

Materials

- newspapers from different places, published on the same day
- newspapers from the same place, published different days
- copies of a daily paper for each student in your class

Vocabulary

The vocabulary listed includes meanings as they pertain to the newspaper.

banner - headline across the top of a page

byline - story's source

caption - copy about photograph

copy - all written material

dateline - where, when written

ears - boxes on front page in the top corners

flag - name of paper (and sometimes publisher), date volume, etc.

headline - gives story's main idea

index - gives contents location

jump line - tells where to find the rest of the story

jump page - last page, where most stories are continued

lead story - most important story in the last 24 hours

masthead - box that lists newspaper information (ie: publisher, subscription, costs, etc.)

second front - first page of the second section

wire service - (see Communication, Activity and Vocabulary)

Communication

Getting to Know the Newspaper continued

Preparation

Obtain several copies of newspapers:

1) published in different places on the same day,

2) published in the same place but on different days.

Read the daily paper you will give to class before distributing it.

Background Information

A daily routing may be unchanging, but a newspaper, even though printed daily, is ever-changing. The only unchanged thing in a daily paper is its components such as its flag, index, features, etc. The news it prints each day depends on the events of the past 24 hours.

Newspapers can be more informative and permanent than other forms of communication. They usually give more information than radio or television, yet they are sometimes abbreviated (edited) because of available space. They offer the reader an opportunity to be discriminating. Rather than sitting through an entire newscast, a newspaper reader may first scan the paper to see what he or she wants to read and then go back and read the articles of interest. A paper may be read at one's convenience.

Many newspapers offer educational programs to familiarize students with newspapers and to develop their skills in scanning, reading and critical thinking.

Teaching Suggestions

• Ask your students how many of them read the newspaper, how often, what they read, etc. Through such a discussion, you will be able to determine how many of the suggested activities that follow have to do with the class. Whatever you do, do not do all of them at the same time.

• Show students a copy of one newspaper. Go through it with them, page by page, pointing out its elements. (See Vocabulary.) Use a yellow marker to highlight each element. Use a black marker to label each one. When it is marked, leave the paper so it is accessible for the students to use as a reference.

• Show students several newspapers from different places but published the same day. Have them point out each paper's elements and compare their locations in the newspaper. What conclusions can they draw?

• Show students several newspapers from the same place but published on different days. Have them point out the consistencies and differences. What conclusions can they draw?

• Give students the newspapers. They need not all be the same. Let them spend 15-20 minutes looking through the papers to see (1) what some of the content is, (2) what interests them, and (3) what is of no interest to them.

• After they have scanned their papers, ask the students some of the following questions:

1. What would you like to read again or more thoroughly?

2. What did not interest you at all?

3. What first attracted you to something in the paper?

4. Do you know enough about the paper to know what you like or dislike?

5. Was there something you did not get to look at but wish you had had time to?

6. What things in the paper provided information? entertainment? a service? an interpretation?

• Distribute page 36, *Getting to Know the Newspaper* to every student. Tell them they will use it with that day's newspaper.

• Pass out a newspaper to every student.

• After students have completed the worksheet, ask them if they had to read the entire paper to complete the assignment. Explain that what they did is called scanning. Explain that scanning is what someone does when he/she first looks at a newspaper and that this is how he/she focuses in on what is of interest.

Notes/Ideas for Next Time

_____

_____

_____

_____

_____

_____

_____

_____

Similarities and Differences

Name _____

Interpret each of the following sayings. Include an example.

"a chip off the old block" _____

_____

_____

"like night and day" _____

_____

_____

"two peas in a pod" _____

_____

_____

Compare yourself to one person.

Write the name of the person to whom you will compare yourself. _____

Write all the similarities you and that person share. _____

_____

_____

_____

_____

_____

_____

_____

_____

Write the ways in which you and the person are different. _____

_____

_____

_____

_____

_____

_____

_____

Getting to Know the Newspaper

Communication

Name _____

Describe the newspaper's flag. Write exactly what is on it in the box below.

```
┌─────────────────────────────────────────────────────────┐
│                                                           │
│                                                           │
│                                                           │
│                                                           │
│                                                           │
└─────────────────────────────────────────────────────────┘
```

Take a few minutes to look through the paper. List the news articles, features, photographs and advertisements that interested you the most.

1. _____

2. _____

3. _____

4. _____

5. _____

Answer the following questions about this specific issue of the newspaper.

What is the lead story about? _____

_____

Write the headlines for two stories that came from a wire service.

1. _____

2. _____

Write the names of three reporters and the headline of each one's article.

Reporter	Headline
_____	_____
_____	_____
_____	_____

Write the headline of an article that has a dateline. _____

_____

What is its dateline? _____

On which page will you find the Crossword Puzzle? _____ Obituaries? _____ Television Schedule? _____ Comics? _____ Classified Advertising? _____

Which part of the paper helped you know where to find the above?_____

Look back at one of the items you listed as interesting you the most. Write which one it is. _____

Read it thoroughly. On the back of this page, write what it was about or what you liked about it.

Communication

Create a Newspaper

Concepts

- The duties of a newspaper's staff are many.
- It takes many people working together to publish a newspaper.
- A daily newspaper gives a picture beyond the student's world.

Objectives

- To understand how news is collected daily
- To understand how a news article is written and edited
- To understand the mechanics of publishing a newspaper
- To participate in a cooperative learning activity

Materials

news articles, photographs, overhead projector

Vocabulary

The vocabulary listed includes meanings as they pertain to the terminology of newspaper publishing.

boards - one for every page, layouts on them that are camera ready

deadline - the date on which a reporter must have a story in to his/her editor

dummy - sheet of paper with columns showing what the space will be used for in the newspaper - advertising first, rest of articles around ads

editor - (assignment, copy, editorial, feature, managing, news, sports, etc.) decides what will and will not be printed

layout - placement of articles

morgue - reference library of news articles previously printed

news desk - where news editor and managing editor sit

newsroom - editors', photographers', and reporters' work space

paste-up - articles glued to boards after type is set

production meeting - Editors meet to plan the next issue's pages and space allotment.

reporter's beat - usual assignment or area covered by reporter

typesetter - sets type according to importance and space

wire service - organizations that gather news and send it to newspapers

Preparation

- Cut out enough short news articles for every student.
- Look for and save an action-packed photograph. Cut it out without its headline, caption or related article.
- Cut out photographs several weeks ahead of this project. Cut off their headlines, captions and/or related articles.

Background Information

Handwritten news sheets were the first newspapers. They were posted in public places for the public to read. After the invention of the printing press, multiple copies of a newspaper could be more readily produced, but the news still was not communicated long distances. Today with computers, wire services and satellites, news is exchanged and reported all over the world.

Teaching Suggestions

You will want to do the suggested activities that follow over several periods. You know your class. Split the lessons accordingly.

- Explain to students that a news article may be edited several times. When a reporter turns in a story, he or she communicates all the details of the event being reported. An editor in the newsroom usually rewrites it, possibly even several times, so that it will fit into the amount of space allotted for it. Write a sample sentence on the board:

  The city's main water pipe broke downtown and it flooded all the basements and streets in the business district.

  Tell students to rewrite the sentence and use only 11 words. Ask students for suggestions, but tell them they may not change its meaning. Write their responses on the board. Do this type of exercise until you feel students understand the concept.

- Distribute a short newspaper article to every student. Have them expand the article into the long form they think the reporter may have turned in.

- Provide each student with a different photograph without a headline or caption. Tell them to write a headline and caption for their photograph.

- Place a photograph without its headline or caption on an overhead projector.

  1. Have students write an article about it. Make sure they understand it is not to be a caption. They should include every detail.

  2. When they are finished, have some read aloud.

  3. Have students trade articles. Instruct them to rewrite each other's stories by

Communication

Create a Newspaper continued

cutting 25-50 words out of them but still keeping the same meaning.

- After students have an understanding about the newspaper's components and how it is edited, create a front page of a newspaper with them. Tell them you will act as the managing editor and will call a production meeting. They will act as one of the paper's editors at the meeting. Point out the different kinds of editors (Vocabulary) that might be at the meeting.

1. Ask "the editors" for their ideas for front-page stories. Their suggestions should come from current events (ie: yesterday's game, special assembly, field trips, etc.) with which they have some knowledge. Write their suggestions on the board.

2. Have "editors" discuss which stories are worthy of a place on the front page (select three).

3. After they have selected the stories, draw a dummy page with three columns on the board. Ask the "editors" of the selected articles which one they think should be the lead story. When they decide, ask how much space should be devoted to it. Mark out the space on the dummy page. Do this for the other two articles too.

4. Ask the "editors" if they think there should be a photograph with one of the stories. Mark where it will go. (It will cover two columns). You will have to do some rearranging.

5. Ask "editors" if they think all the copy and a photograph will fit on the page. Write jump lines where applicable.

6. Now tell students to pretend they are copy editors in the newsroom and have them suggest headlines for the articles. Explain that after reporters turn in their articles, copy editors edit them and write their headlines.

7. Mark out the next page if you feel students need more practice.

- Divide your class into small groups. Tell them that each group's task will be to produce a 3-4 page newspaper. They may include anything they want, but there should be a variety of items including news, puzzles, sports, etc. If they are going to include photographs, they will have to draw them. They should share in the roles of a newspaper staff. Make page 39, *Create a Newspaper*, available for them to use for dummy sheets and paste-ups. When students are ready to print their papers, they should hand write (print) their articles and cut and paste them to fit in the columns on the worksheet.

- Make enough copies of each group's newspapers for every class member to enjoy.

- Invite a journalist, type-setter, advertising representative, circulation manager, etc., to speak to your class.

- Plan a field trip to a newspaper plant.

Notes/Ideas for Next Time

_____
_____
_____
_____
_____
_____
_____
_____
_____
_____
_____
_____
_____
_____
_____
_____
_____
_____
_____
_____
_____
_____
_____
_____
_____
_____
_____
_____
_____
_____
_____
_____
_____

Create a Newspaper

Communication

Name _____

Getting Dressed in the Morning

Concepts

- Clothes help tell history.
- Clothing changed with the development of trade and technology.
- Clothing once indicated wealth and status.

Objectives

- To be aware of the relationship between peoples' dress and the development of technology and its place in history
- To learn what people were like through the study of their dress
- To develop drawing conclusion skills

Materials

period pictures, sample fabrics

Vocabulary

portrait, textile, names of fabrics, synthetic, styles (apron, breeches, bustle, chaps, kilt, poncho, pinafore, tunic, uniform)

Preparation

- Set up a corner in the room with books about costumes and/or clothing.
- Collect several reproductions of paintings that show people's dress in the past.
- Gather scraps of material long before this activity begins.

Background Information

Clothing includes all the different garments, accessories and decorations worn by people around the world. Clothing is one of people's needs.

Clothing is worn for protection from weather and in work and play activities as a means of identification and for appearance and decoration. In fact, decoration on the body has been more important to people throughout history than the actual items of clothing.

People in different parts of the world wear different types of clothes. This is because people have different reasons for wearing clothes. Also, the material available and how the clothes are made often determine clothing style, and people wear different clothes according to custom.

Teaching Suggestions

- You may want to do the exercises suggested, or you could do part of them with each period in history your class studies, (ie: Ancient Times, Middle Ages, Revolutionary War, industrial Revolution, etc.) or this activity could stand alone.
- Ask students to name articles of clothing familiar to them. After that, ask if they have ever heard of any of the styles listed in Vocabulary and who wore them or when they were worn.
- Ask students to name articles of clothing that are worn for protection (ie: coats, helmets, wet suits, etc.), identification (social status, uniforms, etc.) and appearance (ie: jewelry, scarves, ties, etc.).
- Display pictures of people from the past (or from the period being studied). Use them to point out different styles and to motivate a discussion. Ask some of the following questions:

1. How is it possible to know what clothes of the past looked like when many of them no longer are in existence?

2. What kind of a life did the people wearing the clothes in the pictures live?

3. Were the clothes practical? Were they easy to move in? Were they "everyday" clothes?

4. Specifically about portraits ask: Who could afford to have a portrait painted? What did these people do? (Tell students that most people dressed in clothing much simpler than that worn by the wealthy and could not afford to have paintings made of themselves.)

- Draw the time line below on the board or on wrapping paper. Have students decide in what period of time each picture was painted. Or, have students draw pictures of costumes at different times in history and place them along the time line.

3000 B.C. -Ancient Times: Clothes were long and draped over bodies loosely.

400 A.D. - Middle Ages: tighter fitting clothes

1300 - 1500 - Renaissance: elaborate clothes for wealthy

1600 - formal dress begins to ease

1700 - Spinning Jenny and Spinning Mule changed how cloth was made.

1800 - Industrial Revolution: plainer clothes, less hand-made clothing

1900 - improved manufacturing; shortened hems, sportswear; synthetic materials

Getting Dressed in the Morning continued

Costume

- Set up a textile center. Let students handle different fabrics, learn their names and how they feel.

- Instruct students to write about the clothing of a specific period. Have them dress in clothing of that period and report to the group. (Some period clothing may be available from a costume rental store, but encourage students to be creative.)

- Arrange for a trip to a museum that displays costumes of certain periods.

- Art Projects:

  1. Make collages using material scraps and decorative sequins and ribbons.

  2. Draw a fashion ad for a magazine or newspaper.

  3. Draw a picture of what clothes might look like in the future.

- At any time during this activity, distribute the worksheet. It is self-explanatory and informative. Have students complete it. Discuss it afterwards.

- Supply students with clothes of today and yesterday. Have them run races putting the clothes on over the clothes they have on. (Only shoes may be removed to make getting clothes on easier.)

Notes/Ideas for Next Time

_____

_____

_____

_____

_____

_____

_____

Costume

Getting Dressed in the Morning

Name _____

Imagine if you had lived about 200 years ago how long it would have taken you to dress. What boys and girls put on each day is listed below.

Girls

1. undershirt
2. tight bodice with little buttons
3. garter belt to hold up stockings
4. long stockings
5. long pants buttoned to bodice
6. high buttoned shoes
7. long petticoat
8. another starched petticoat
9. long dress
10. pinafore
11. bonnet

Boys

1. undershirt
2. long underpants
3. shirt with buttons
4. sometimes a tie
5. long black stockings
6. pants buttoned onto shirt
7. high-buttoned boots
8. vest or waistcoat with buttons
9. jacket
10. hat

Write the clothing items you put on in the morning below in the order in which you put them on.

1. _____
2. _____
3. _____
4. _____
5. _____
6. _____

What is the hardest thing for you to put on? _____

What is the easiest? _____ Time yourself one day. How long does it take you to dress? _____

Why is it easier to dress today than long ago? _____

_____

Look around your class. What are the most popular types of clothing? _____

_____

How do boys and girls today dress alike? _____

_____

How is their dress different? _____

Middle Ages

Heraldry

Concepts

- Heraldry symbolizes a person, group, institution, etc.
- Heraldry is displayed as a coat of arms on a shield.
- A coat of arms is unique.
- Heraldry is a means of identification.
- Heraldry has a language and rules.

Objectives

- To develop an image of self, family, school, class, community, etc.
- To translate image from fact to symbol
- To follow the rules of heraldry (follow directions)

Materials

paints, brushes, colored bristol board or construction paper, scissors, patterns, student directions, pencils

Vocabulary

The vocabulary listed includes meanings as they pertain to the language of heraldry.

arms - short for coat of arms

heraldry - system of symbols used to represent individuals, families, institutions, countries, etc.

herald - checks authenticity and sets heraldic rules

shield - main part of coat of arms

field - surface of the shield

crest - object placed on top of crown, coronet or wreath; coat of arms can exist without crest but not vice-versa

crown, coronet, wreath - emblem of wearer: crest rests on it: on top of helmet

helmet (helm) - shows rank of bearer

mantling - cape attached to helmet or draped around shield

supporters - creatures on either side of shields

motto - below shield, called the device

insignias - special honors; not hereditary; around shield

cadency - status symbols of individual members in a family

achievement of arms - whole display including shield, helmet, crest, mantling, supporters, etc.

blazon - heraldic language (description of heraldry)

tinctures - hues used in heraldry: **colors, metals, furs - colors** - red, blue, black, green, purple - **metals** - gold represented by yellow, silver represented by white

furs - ermine (black spots on white), vair (alternating blue and white stripes)

charges - decorations or symbols used; two kinds:
1) ordinaries - main charges; geometric shapes
2) animate - beasts, monsters, birds, etc.

Preparation

Use an opaque projector to enlarge the patterns on page 45 for the students to trace around to make their personal coats of arms. Make the shield as large as the piece of paper or bristol board they will be using. Make the charges proportionate to the shield's size. You will want to make three sizes of the templates: one that will fit the shield, two that will fit on the shield, four that will fit on the shield. Cut several templates of each size out of a light cardboard.

Look for and collect coats of arms (ie: Queen of England, corporations, etc.).

Background Information

Heraldry originated so knights in battle could be recognized. In battle, it was difficult to tell a friend from a foe behind armor, so identifying coats of arms were painted on each knight's shield and flag.

At first, the coats of arms were simple, but as more people assumed arms, they became more complicated. In order to avoid duplication, a College of Arms was established to monitor the choices of arms and to set rules for their design. A group of men called heralds ran the college.

Later, heraldry became a system of identification for members of the upper class. They identified their possessions by marking them with their coats of arms. (Common people did not have arms.) There was also a need for the recognition of knights as they carried messages between kingdoms and/or armies. Heralds needed to recognize knights too when they directed tournaments or conducted ceremonies. Family coats of arms of the upper class were passed down from generation to generation on the male side, but special honors on the coat of arms were not hereditary and had to be dropped. However, each individual who inherited the arms could add personal symbols and emblems to the coat of arms.

Teaching Suggestions

- Talk about how coats of arms started and the direction they took. The *Encyclopedia Britannica* is a good teacher source from which to learn about heraldry.

    43

Middle Ages

Heraldry continued

• Use an overhead projector to show a coat of arms. Go over all its elements, what they are called, and their meaning with the students.

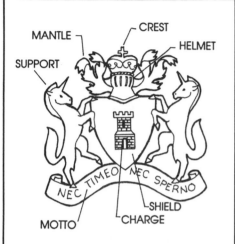

MANTLE
CREST
HELMET
SUPPORT
NEC TIMEO NEC SPERNO
MOTTO
SHIELD
CHARGE

• Display other coats of arms on the projector. Have students point out the elements. Discuss their symbols, and why they were probably selected.

• Ask students to look for coats of arms and bring copies of them to school. Make a bulletin board display of them.

• Art Projects:
1. Suggest students design their own coat of arms (a full achievement including the shield, crest, helmet, mantle, supporters, etc.).

• Discuss things students might put on their shields. Some items might refer to their name, where they live, the occupation of someone in their family, interests, etc. They may need some assistance getting started, but once you feel they have an idea of what they are going to do, pass out the worksheet (pages 46 and 47).

• Go over the sheet with them. Explain that only certain colors are allowed in

heraldry, and certain ones may not be put on one another. A color may not be put on a color (red, blue, black, green, purple). A metal may not be put on a metal (gold or yellow - silver or white). A fur may not be put on a fur (black on white - white on blue).

• Have students sketch the designs of their coat of arms first and indicate the colors they will use. Check their designs to make sure they followed the rules about colors. When all students' designs are correct, make the materials they will need available and tell them to make their coats of arms following the directions on pages 46 and 47.

•• Make a blanket coat of arms. When all the coats of arms are finished, mount them on the same size, but different colored sheets of paper (ie: 18" x 24"). Tape the papers together from the back. Hang the "blanket" over a table or hang it up. (A knight would put the blanket over his horse marked with his coat of arms.)

2. Have students design a coat of arms for the class, school, or community.

3. Have students make pennons, the triangular flags the knights carried on their lances, and put their coats of arms on them. Hang each pennon from the ceiling above each student's desk.

4. Following the directions on pages 48 and 49, students can make miniature knights on horses. You should make one as an example. Give students the directions. Provide the necessary

materials and have students complete the project independently.

Materials needed per student: egg carton, scissors, small jewelry box, small cardboard box, down feathers, foil, glue

• You may want to suggest that students make a shield or a coat of arms for their knights.

• Suggest students write stories about their knights. Display the knights with their stories alongside them.

• Foot soldiers and castles could also be made from egg boxes. Have students make a medieval scene.

• Discuss what mottos are. Have students write a personal motto to add to their coat of arms.

• Arrange for a trip to a museum where students may see some items related to the Middle Ages. Arrange to have a guide lead the tour.

A. Visit an art museum. View pictures of the times. Encourage students to observe the stories they tell.

B. Visit a history museum. See the costumes of the times. Listen to a talk about heraldry.

Notes/Ideas for Next Time

_____
_____
_____
_____
_____
_____
_____
_____
_____
_____

Patterns

Middle Ages

Name _____

Making a Coat of Arms

Middle Ages

Name _____

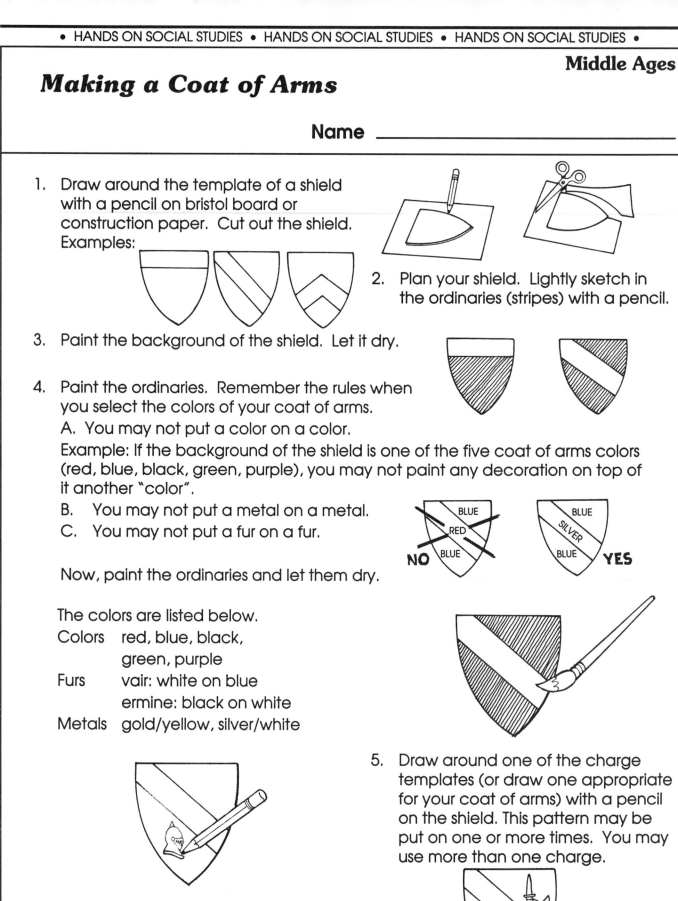

1. Draw around the template of a shield with a pencil on bristol board or construction paper. Cut out the shield. Examples:

2. Plan your shield. Lightly sketch in the ordinaries (stripes) with a pencil.

3. Paint the background of the shield. Let it dry.

4. Paint the ordinaries. Remember the rules when you select the colors of your coat of arms.

   A. You may not put a color on a color.

   Example: If the background of the shield is one of the five coat of arms colors (red, blue, black, green, purple), you may not paint any decoration on top of it another "color".

   B. You may not put a metal on a metal.

   C. You may not put a fur on a fur.

   Now, paint the ordinaries and let them dry.

   The colors are listed below.

   Colors   red, blue, black, green, purple

   Furs   vair: white on blue
             ermine: black on white

   Metals   gold/yellow, silver/white

5. Draw around one of the charge templates (or draw one appropriate for your coat of arms) with a pencil on the shield. This pattern may be put on one or more times. You may use more than one charge.

6. Paint the charges. Remember the rules. Let them dry.

46

Middle Ages

Making a Coat of Arms continued

Name _____

7. Draw the supporters you want for your coat of arms on construction paper. The animate objects you select do not have to be the same, but they should face each other (in the opposite directions) - one to the left and one to the right.

8. Draw the supporters' features (ie: eyes, crown, collar, etc.) on the color of construction paper you want for each one. Paste them on the supporters.

9. Paste the supporters onto the shield, one on each side.

10. Follow steps 7, 8, and 9 to make the crest, coronet (crown or wreath), mantle and motto.

HELP THOSE IN NEED

When everything is in place, you have made a full coat of arms called an achievement. Describe your coat of arms below and the meanings of your choices. In heraldry language, this would be called the blazon.

_____

_____

_____

_____

_____

_____

_____

_____

_____

_____

_____

_____

A Knight and His Horse

Middle Ages

Name _____

1. Cut out two cups from an egg carton. Trim around them.

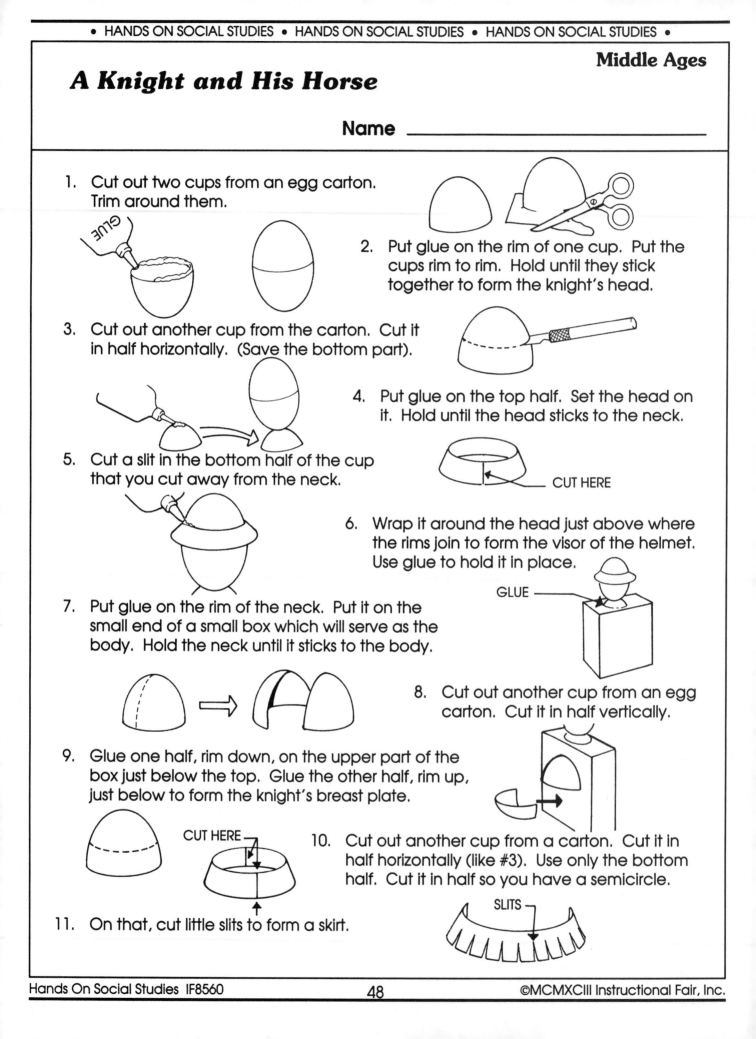

2. Put glue on the rim of one cup. Put the cups rim to rim. Hold until they stick together to form the knight's head.

3. Cut out another cup from the carton. Cut it in half horizontally. (Save the bottom part).

4. Put glue on the top half. Set the head on it. Hold until the head sticks to the neck.

5. Cut a slit in the bottom half of the cup that you cut away from the neck.

CUT HERE

6. Wrap it around the head just above where the rims join to form the visor of the helmet. Use glue to hold it in place.

GLUE

7. Put glue on the rim of the neck. Put it on the small end of a small box which will serve as the body. Hold the neck until it sticks to the body.

8. Cut out another cup from an egg carton. Cut it in half vertically.

9. Glue one half, rim down, on the upper part of the box just below the top. Glue the other half, rim up, just below to form the knight's breast plate.

CUT HERE

10. Cut out another cup from a carton. Cut it in half horizontally (like #3). Use only the bottom half. Cut it in half so you have a semicircle.

11. On that, cut little slits to form a skirt.

SLITS

Middle Ages

A Knight and His Horse continued

Name _____

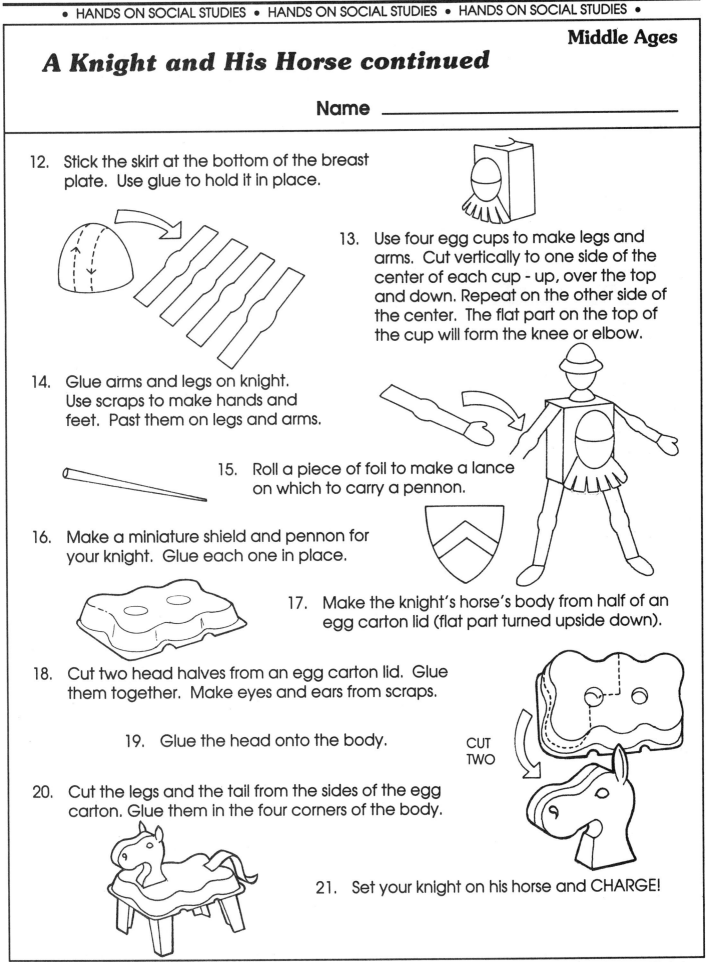

12. Stick the skirt at the bottom of the breast plate. Use glue to hold it in place.

13. Use four egg cups to make legs and arms. Cut vertically to one side of the center of each cup - up, over the top and down. Repeat on the other side of the center. The flat part on the top of the cup will form the knee or elbow.

14. Glue arms and legs on knight. Use scraps to make hands and feet. Past them on legs and arms.

15. Roll a piece of foil to make a lance on which to carry a pennon.

16. Make a miniature shield and pennon for your knight. Glue each one in place.

17. Make the knight's horse's body from half of an egg carton lid (flat part turned upside down).

18. Cut two head halves from an egg carton lid. Glue them together. Make eyes and ears from scraps.

19. Glue the head onto the body.

CUT TWO

20. Cut the legs and the tail from the sides of the egg carton. Glue them in the four corners of the body.

21. Set your knight on his horse and CHARGE!

The Meaning of Money

Economics

Concepts

- Money has different value and importance for different people.
- Money buys different things for different people according to needs.
- Needs may be different at different times in a person's life.

Objectives

- To recognize money may mean different things to different people
- To learn how to manage money

Materials

ledger

Vocabulary

budget, income, means, ledger, fixed expenses

Preparation

Make copies of Activity Sheet I ahead of time. Cut it in half along the dotted line. You will use the upper half at least three times more than the bottom half.

Background Information

Financial planning is no different than planning for an event such as a trip or scavenger hunt. Advance planning avoids problems. Living within one's means is possible if one knows how much money he or she has and allots it accordingly. Basic needs should be considered first when setting up a budget.

Teaching Suggestions

- Tell students to imagine that they found $5 on the side of a country road. There were no homes or people anywhere in sight. Ask what they would do with it. List their responses on a large sheet of paper under a heading, "You and $5".
- Take down the list described above and put it aside. Put up more sheets of paper and present the same situation as above ($5 found on country road) but ask different questions (see below). Write students' responses under the headings in parentheses below after the question on each sheet.

  1. What do you think a person who was out of work and had a family would do with the $5? ("Poor Person and $5").

  2. What might your mother or father do if they found it? ("Mom or Dad and $5").

  3. What might a very wealthy person do with it? ("Wealthy Person and $5").

- Put up all four sheets. Discuss the differences and the reasons for these differences. Include the age of the finder, need, amount of personal wealth, etc. in your discussion.
- Explain that many people have a budget. It is determined by their needs and the amount of money they have to spend. Some people keep a ledger that shows their fixed expenses, income, outlay and the totals in all of these categories.
- Show students a ledger and how entries are made, amounts are totaled, etc.
- Ask students what some fixed expenses might be.
- Distribute the top part of the worksheet. Tell students to keep a record of their money for a week. They should record all that they receive and all that is spent. Make sure they understand the sources. Ask which ones might occur on a more regular basis.
- Do the above for at least one more week.
- At the end of two weeks or more, discuss the outcome of students' record-keeping. Ask if they lived within their means, what their needs were, and if they need to make any adjustments in order to live within their means.
- Based on each individual's intake and outlay, tell students they are going to set up a budget and try to live within it. Distribute the lower part of the worksheet. Tell students to look at their intake-outlay records on the budget form for the past weeks and to write in the category names (ie: entertainment, food, hobbies, toys, savings, miscellaneous, other, etc.) in which they spent their money. Then, have them fill in the source form above it. After that, have them write the amount of money they will allow themselves to spend in each category on the budget form. Caution them not to spend more than they will take in.
- Distribute a spending form (top part). Tell them to keep track of their spending again for a week.
- At the end of the week, ask them to see how successfully they lived within their budget.

Economics

The Meaning of Money

Name _____

Sources of Income for the Week of _____

	Allowance	Earnings	Gifts	Other	Total
Amounts					

Recording of Spending for the Week of _____

Day 1	
Day 2	
Day 3	
Day 4	
Day 5	
Day 6	
Day 7	

Sources of Income for the Week of _____

	Allowance	Earnings	Gifts	Other	Total
Amounts					

Budget for the Week of _____

Categories							Total
Amounts							

51

Consumer and Producer

Concepts

- Consumption and production are the two elements that make up the economy.
- Consumers use goods and services.
- Producers supply consumers' needs.
- Consumers keep workers employed.

Objectives

- To understand the components that make up the economy
- To realize that it is the consumers' needs that decide what will be produced
- To identify consumers and producers
- To make some consumer decisions

Materials

newspaper advertising

Vocabulary

consumer, producer, economy, supply, demand

Preparation

Collect several days of newspaper ads. Put them up on a bulletin board. Make a sign. Cut out letters that read, "GENERAL STORE". Put the sign above the advertisement bulletin board.

Background Information

What consumers spend money on affects what is produced. Consumer spending keeps workers producing. Consumers can be individuals or businesses. Producers can be businesses and individual workers.

Before America was an industrialized nation, the consumer and the producer were one and the same. For example, the farmer (consumer) decided what crops to grow or which animals to raise (producer). Today, individuals are both but not under the same roof. They sell their services (producers) in the work place. The money they earn frees them to choose (consumers) the products they want from suppliers (producers).

Teaching Suggestions

- Help students understand that what a consumer (user) demands, a producer supplies. If there is no demand for a product, a producer may cut the supply. Ask students what effect this could have on the economy.

- Have a discussion about consumers and producers. Ask some of the following questions:
  When are you a consumer? producer?
  Are members of your family consumers or producers?
  Can consumers be producers and producers be consumers?
  Do producers always manufacture products?
  What must one have usually to be a consumer?
  How does one obtain it (money)? What is a person when he works for it?
  Give examples of businesses as consumers? producers?

- Present the following situations or make up some of your own. Ask students to tell if you are describing a consumer or a producer. If the answer is a consumer, ask what is being consumed. If the answer is a producer, ask what the product is.
  The (office's) telephone bill was over $100.
  Some (nurses) work twelve hour shifts.
  After (lumberjacks) cut trees, they send them to the mill.
  The lumber yard sold the wood to the (builder).
  The (store) gave balloons to its shoppers.

- Help students understand the law of supply and demand. As cost rises, the supply increases. As cost comes down, the supply is less. Tell students you are going to ask some questions that they should answer as consumers. Turn their attention to the store bulletin board. Have them pretend that it is a store, that the advertisements are its wares, and that they are shoppers. Formulate questions so students' answers will most often reflect a lower cost.
  Examples of possible questions:
  Which dog collar would you buy?
  What meat would you buy for dinner?
  What would you buy to keep your hands warm? etc.
  Form a consensus from students' answers. Ask why most chose what they did.

- Ask what can happen when there is an oversupply of goods (sale, slow down in manufacturing), or when there is an increased demand (prices up, greater production).

- Ask what causes for demand might be (fad, need, seasonal, etc.).

- While distributing the Consumer and Producer Activity Sheet, give students instructions to complete it. They should be able to do it independently, but offer assistance if necessary. Provide a stack of newspaper advertisements for this activity.

- After completion, discuss students' independent conclusions.

Consumer and Products

Economics

Name _____

Write five ways in which you are a consumer.

_____

_____

_____

_____

_____

Write five ways in which you, or someone you know, is a producer.

_____

_____

_____

_____

_____

Write the names of three businesses you know of that are producers.

_____

Write the names of three businesses you know of that are both consumers and producers. Tell how each one is both.

_____ consumer _____

(company)   producer _____

_____ consumer _____

(company)   producer _____

_____ consumer _____

(company)   producer _____

Look at newspaper advertisements. Find one that shows there is probably an over-supply. Attach it in the space to the right. What makes you think there is an over-supply?

_____

Look at newspaper advertisements again. Find one that shows there is probably a big demand for a particular product. Attach it in the space to the left. What makes you think there is a big demand? _____

_____

53

The Stock Market

Concepts

- Corporations can get started and expand by issuing stock to get money.
- Most large businesses are owned by outside investors.
- Investors hope to make money when they buy stock in a business.
- Investors and corporations buy and sell stock through the stock market.

Objectives

- To recognize the names of several large corporations and their products
- To understand how investors may buy and sell shares of corporations
- To understand how corporations may offer stock on the stock market
- To realize big business needs money from outside sources
- To realize corporations are often public

Materials

financial sections of the newspaper

Vocabulary

AMEX, bond, commission, corporation, dividend, interest, investors, NYSE, profits, securities, share, stock, stockbroker, stock certificate, stockholders, stock market, Wall Street

Preparation

Order newspapers (financial section only if possible) for the days you will want to use them. Some days, you will want one for every student (or every pair of students). On other days, two or three copies will be enough.

Background Information

A few businessmen started the stock market in 1792 in New York City. They wanted an organization that would make it possible for investors to buy and sell companies. Rules were established and the stock market became the agent for buyers and sellers who paid a commission for its services. Its initial concept continues today.

When a person or a group of people want to start a business or company, they need money. So, they issue stock, sold in units called shares, which is sold to investors who want to buy a part of a business or company. This transaction takes place at the stock market where stock brokers put the two parties together.

The stock market is not located in just one place. It is a network of brokerage houses throughout the world that connects businessmen with investors and vice versa. These institutions are connected by computers and phone lines that enable them to trade their securities.

Teaching Suggestions

- Ask students why they think anyone would want to own a part of someone else's business (to make money). Explain how investors could make money: profit from sales, dividends, interest.
- Ask students if any of them have ever had a business (ie: lemonade stand, raked leaves, run errands, etc.). How did they get started? Chances are they used what was already in their homes and did not borrow money to get started, but ask them to imagine that they did. What would they need? How much would they need to borrow? Where would they get the money? How would they pay it back? Would they pay it back at one time, or would they reinvest some of it? Would they pay interest or dividends?
- Ask students to name large national or international companies they have heard about. Make a list of them on the board.
- Pick one of the companies as an example. Ask students to list some of the positions of the workers (ie: GM - assembly workers, welders, designers, foremen, etc.). Point out that these people may own a part of the company, but much of it is probably owned by outside investors called stock holders.
- Help students realize that many things they consume or use are products of large companies (ie: cars, appliances, food, etc.). Give them a homework assignment. Have students look on their kitchen shelves and around their homes for products produced by national or international companies. Tell them to write the names of three companies and their products they found at home and to bring their lists to school.
- Collect the students' lists. Make a composite list on the board or make copies for every student.
- Distribute copies of a newspaper's financial section to every student or to pairs of students. Have students first

Economics

The Stock Market continued

turn to the report of the New York Stock Exchange (NYSE) to see how many of the corporations they found at home are listed on the "big board". For each one listed, note the abbreviation of the company's name. Then, explain what each entry before and after the stock's name means. (All headings may not be appropriate for your class. Teach those that are.) Before the stock's name, the high and low prices for the stock for the year so far are given. The stock's name is followed by how much money (dividend) is paid in a year, the percentage this is of the going price, the number of sales in the 100's, high, low and closing cost per share for that day, and what the net change was, if any. The closing, or last cost, will be the opening cost the next day.

- On another day, do the same as above on the American Exchange (AMEX) or over the counter for those stocks not found on the NYSE.

- Have students select a corporation they would like to learn about. Have them research it. They can write the company for annual reports, for its prospectus or for information about it.

- Do one or both of the following activities. Your choice will depend on where you teach.
  1. A) Have students pick a stock to watch. It may be one of the above or another of their choosing.
  b) Distribute *The Stock Market* (page 56). Tell students to fill in the top of the page as

though they bought the stock they chose to watch. Have them follow the stock for a month, fill in the activity sheet each day, and on the last day, have them fill in the bottom part.
  2. With the help of a stockbroker, you select a stock whose cost is not too high nor risky. Ask students if they would like to participate in the experience of buying one share of stock. Make it strictly optional. Warn them that they could lose money. If they decide to participate, tell them to bring in no more than one dollar towards its purchase. Buy one share in your name. When the stock certificate arrives, show it to the class. Issue each student a certificate (page 57) stating his or her share (24 participants = 1/24 shares) in the upper right hand corner. Each certificate number in the upper left hand corner should be different. Sign and date the certificates. Tell students to keep their certificates in a safe place so they have them when it is time to sell. Follow the stock all year. When a dividend is paid, put it in the "bank". At the end of the year, sell the stock. Divide the sale money plus the dividends among the participants.

- Take students to visit a local brokerage house. Let them see the ticker-tape in action and a stockbroker at his/her desk working with a computer.

Notes/Ideas for Next Time

_____

_____

_____

_____

_____

_____

_____

_____

_____

_____

_____

_____

_____

_____

_____

_____

_____

_____

_____

_____

_____

_____

_____

_____

_____

_____

_____

_____

Economics

The Stock Market

Name _____

Name of stock _____

Number of shares bought _____ Date bought _____

Price paid per share _____ Total cost _____

For the next 20 days, look at the stock market report in the newspaper. Record your stock's financial activities under the appropriate column.

Date	Year High	Year Low	Dividend	Daily %	Sales in 100s	High	Low	Close	Net Change

On what dates were more shares of your stock traded? _____

On what date (in the past month) was it at its highest? _____

If you had sold it that day, how much money would you have gotten? _____

What would your profit have been? _____

On what date was your stock at its lowest? _____

If you had sold it on that day, how much money would you have gotten? _____

What would your loss have been? _____

OFFICIAL SEAL

This certifies that _____ is the

owner of _____ shares of _____ .

This certificate is non-transferable without

the said owner's signature on the back of

this document.

signature _____

date _____

©MCMXCIII Instructional Fair, Inc.

In My Suitcase

Concepts

- New kinds of transportation evolved as America expanded.
- The easier moving became, the more people could move.

Objectives

- To understand the correlation between the development of transportation and need
- To develop sequencing skills
- To develop research skills
- To draw conclusions

Materials

shelf paper, markers

Vocabulary

canal boat, flat boat, canals

Preparation

- Collect pictures of different kinds of transportation settlers used in America from the time of the *Mayflower* to date.
- With the help of your school and/or community librarian, set up a transportation corner in your room where students may conduct their research.

Background Information

Boats brought settlers to the New World in the 17th century. After long and difficult journeys, the settlers landed on America's east coast. Since immediate land transportation was difficult, they made their new homes where they landed.

Eventually, some settlers wanted to move on. Sailing along the coast was the easiest way to travel, but some settlers wanted to move inland. They had to walk, ride horseback or travel in horse-drawn wagons. The only direction to travel in the new country where the land was untouched was west, but not until after the War of 1812 did

American settlers begin to move farther distances in that direction. Good farmland, waters filled with fish and forests full of game beyond the Appalachian Mountains lured many settlers.

The westward movement expanded as the pioneers continued to move and settle all the land between America's east and west coasts. The modes of transportation varied according to the distances traveled, the stage of development transportation was in and the origin and destination of the move.

Teaching Suggestions

- Put up a bulletin board entitled, "Getting Around in America". Leave it blank until you have had a brainstorming session with students. Then, put up pictures of different kinds of transportation.

- Brainstorm with your class. Ask students to cite as many types of transportation as they can. Write them on the board.

- On the students' list, circle the modes of travel that have been a part of America's expansion (ie: sailing ships, horses, wagons, stagecoaches, canal boats, flat boats, steamboats, covered wagons, train cars, planes).

- With students, make a time line on shelf paper depicting the impact that development of transportation had on the growth of America. Dates are not necessary at this time. Just have them sequence what types were used and the reasons for their order.

- Then, have students research and put dates on the time line. Have them draw pictures of the different vehicles on the time line.

- Discuss some of the following:
  1) Possessions settlers could

transport and why.
  2) How modes of transportation, distance, terrain covered, time of journey, etc., determined needs and what could be transported.
  3) When, why and how moving became easier.

- Distribute *In My Suitcase* (pages s 59 and 60). Explain what is to be done. More than one kind of transportation might have been used (ie: walking, horseback, boats, etc.) in one move depending on the destination, time, distance and difficulty. The area marked means the length of the move. Tell them to use the transportation corner to do the necessary research to complete these activity sheets. This activity may be done individually - where every student does each page in its entirety. Or, students could be divided into small groups. Make each group responsible for one of the trips.

- After the worksheets are complete, discuss the students' findings. Ask what some hardships were or are. Ask any students who have moved to compare their move with some of those on the worksheets.

- Divide students into groups. Have them act out each journey.

- Take students on one of the trips (ie: the Santa Fe Trail). Have them take clothes, bring provisions and necessary equipment, etc. A part of each day should be spent on the trail. Make up situations (ie: Indian attack, storm, broken wheel axle, etc.) that students have to contend with. Cook a meal each day on the trail.

Transportation

In My Suitcase

Name _____

From - To	Year	Type of Transportation	Time
England to America	1620		

My family packed _____

_____

_____

_____

_____

| Boston, MA to Providence, RI | 1700 | | |

My family packed _____

_____

_____

_____

_____

| New York City to Albany, NY | 1815 | | |

My family packed _____

_____

_____

_____

_____

| Albany, NY to Buffalo, NY | 1830 | | |

My family packed _____

_____

_____

_____

In My Suitcase continued

Name _____

From - To	Year	Type of Transportation	Time
Franklin, MO to Sante Fe, NM	1840		

My family packed _____
_____
_____
_____
_____

Omaha, NE to Sacramento, CA	1880		

My family packed _____
_____
_____
_____
_____

Franklin, MO to Santa Fe, NM	1945		

My family packed _____
_____
_____
_____
_____

England to America	1995		

My family packed _____
_____
_____
_____
_____

Getting Involved

Concepts

- Politics is the skill of getting elected to office and being successful once elected.
- Politics exist at several levels of government.
- Politics requires maneuvering and listening to all sides of an issue.
- Working in a group requires cooperation and the use of political skills.

Objectives

- To be able to formulate opinions and defend them
- To realize all people have a responsibility to be active in politics even if they are too young to vote
- To care about things that affect our lives

Materials

sample ballots, voter registration card, current newspapers

Vocabulary

campaign, candidate, constituent, incumbent, local or general election, office, platform, politics, poll, primaries, register, town meeting, fanfare

Preparation

Ask the local election commissioner's office for a voter registration card, a ballot of the upcoming election, and a portable voting tablet with stylus if available. Make enough copies of the voter registration card for each student. Make copies similar to the ballot and mark it "unofficial". If possible, videotape current political commercials. Save articles about elections in foreign countries.

Background Information

Electing people to office in early America was carried out with less fanfare than now. Distances between communities, poor transportation and no electronic communication devices made the whirlwind campaigning of today almost nonexistent. Candidates had no staffs, no planned strategies, nor any money for publicity. Their ideas, beliefs and hopes for what they would accomplish in the position they were seeking were most likely imparted through town meetings, word of mouth and just knowing and trusting the candidate.

Today in American politics, a candidate's private and public life is on view whether he/she is running for a local or a national office. From the moment a person decides to run for office, the candidate's faults are exposed by opponents and his/her assets are lauded by supporters. A declared candidate campaigns vigorously, sometimes for months, among constituents to get his or her message across. A lot of time and money is spent today campaigning for office.

Politics is not just the act of getting elected to a government office. Once candidates are elected, they must do a good job and listen to the people they represent or face defeat in the next election.

Teaching Suggestions

- Do the following activity so it coincides with an election - local, state, federal or presidential. This will make it more relevant and easier to do some of the other activities listed.

- Tell students they are about to participate in some political activities - one of which will be to vote. In order to vote, students must be registered. Have them fill out the registration card to see that they are part of a county, township, precinct, etc. Collect the cards when they are completed and keep them for a later activity.

- This would be an appropriate time to explain that although students are not old enough to vote, they are old enough to be interested in and make a difference in the world around them. Hold a discussion about the ways in which they might participate even though they are too young to vote. Some suggestions follow:

1. Students can help make their city, county, state a better place in which to live. Ask them what improvements they would like to see and how they might go about getting them done.

2. Working for a candidate in which they believe is another way for students to be involved. Ask them what kinds of things they might do to help get the candidate elected.

3. Students can defend one side of an issue or law. Ask them to list some issues or laws and tell what they might do to work for or against them. Explain that the above situations require political skill and maneuvering.

- Ask students what they think can happen if people do not

Getting Involved continued

take an interest in their government officials or actions.

- Give students current newspapers to look through specifically for articles about an upcoming election. Discuss what kind it will be, when it will be held and what issues will be voted on in the election.

- Give the following homework assignments:

   1. Listen to the radio or watch television and listen for commercials pertaining to the election.

   2. Look in the newspaper for more articles or advertisements. Bring them in to fill a bulletin board with all the articles.

   3. Look for other evidence related to the election (yard signs, flyers, etc.).

   Discuss the pros and cons of what students saw or heard. Show a videotape of a commercial if possible. Critique it.

- Ask a person involved in the upcoming election to visit your class.

   1. Have a government official speak about an upcoming bond issue, community concern, etc.

   2. Let board of education candidates and/or members tell of future plans for the school district, listen to student concerns and answer students' questions.

- Take students to the office of the election commissioners to see behind the scenes in the voting procedure.

- Show students articles about elections in foreign countries. Discuss them. Point out how

long it takes before they know the results of their elections.

- Distribute the pages 63 and 64, *Getting Involved*. First, divide students into the sides they favor in the upcoming election. Then, make three or four subgroups out of each. Have the subgroups do the activity sheets together. When they are finished, have each group present theirs.

- Go over our voting procedure. Explain a voting booth. Show them the stylus and tablet and how the card and ballot fit on it. Point out that some places still mark a ballot with a pencil. Remind students that in places where the stylus is used, the ballots are machine counted, making the results known sooner. Compare this to foreign countries.

- Hold an election. Do it before the upcoming one. Have students sign their names on a slip of paper. Compare their signatures with their voter registration cards. Give them a ballot to fill out with a pencil and put in a ballot box. Make the results known as quickly as possible.

- Compare the class' results with the actual results after the election.

Notes/Ideas for Next Time

_____

_____

_____

_____

_____

_____

_____

Politics

Getting Involved

Name _____

Work together. Do all the activities on this page and the next. Make the voters vote the way you believe. Be ready to present your ideas to the class.

Make a telephone call on behalf of a candidate and the views you share on a certain topic. Write out what you might say.

Hello. My name is _____

I am calling to ask you to _____

_____

_____

because _____

_____

_____

Please vote next _____

Thank you for your consideration.

Goodbye.

Create a newspaper advertisement.

Write a slogan.

_____

Write a letter to the editor expressing your views about a particular candidate and his/her views on a particular issue.

Dear _____ ,

_____

_____

_____

_____

_____

_____

_____

_____

_____

Make a poster, button and flyer on other sheets of paper.

Politics

Getting Involved continued

Name _____

Create a commercial endorsing a
candidate on a view or an issue
for TV or radio. Act it out.

With another student, debate both sides
of an issue.

Draw an editorial cartoon featuring
a candidate on a view or an issue.

Write an editorial to go with the cartoon.

Write a speech for your issue or candidate.

64

History

Which Is Older?

Concepts

- Situations, customs and objects can change.
- Change may be a result of time, need and/or invention.
- Change is not always better or worse.

Objectives

- To recognize change
- To be aware that things change over time
- To understand why things may change
- To realize all change may not be for the better

Vocabulary

antique, hitching post, outhouse

Preparation

Collect several antique items. Send a note home with students asking if any family has some small items that are no longer used in today's world that they would be willing to share with the class. Ask the same of fellow teachers, family, friends, etc. If you are unable to get any antiques, take slide pictures (ie: washboard, spinning wheel, lady in dress with bustle and bonnet, etc.) from pictures in history or antique books. Also, ask senior citizens in your community if they would like to share items with your class or talk to them about the way things were.

Background Information

A long time ago, life was both easier and harder than it is now. It was easier because people were more self sufficient and there were less demands or needs from society. Therefore, there were not as many things that could go wrong

mechanically. For several reasons, however, life was also more difficult years ago. Travel was inefficient. Communication took a long time. There were no machines to help people do what they needed to do. Many of the clothes people wore back then were not practical. Over the course of many years, people's needs demanded change.

Teaching Suggestions

- Display several antiques. Ask if students know what they are, if they are still used, if they have changed, etc.
- Distribute page 66, *Which is Older?* Help students identify each picture. You know your class best. If students are capable of completing the page independently, assign it. Otherwise, do the page together.
- When the activity sheet is complete, ask students the following questions: (a) Is all change good? Why or why not? (b) What kinds of things change? (c) Why have some things changed?
- Have students list some other ways in which the following areas have changed: fashion, transportation, crop storage, communication, etc.
- Follow-up Activities
  1. Visit an antique shop.
  2. Do one or more of the following:
  a) Assign homework to be done by the light of one candle.
  b) Have an old-fashioned dress-up day. Tell students to study the clothes of a certain period and to dress in this style for an entire school day.
  c) Write with quill pens all day one day.

d) Make butter in a churn.
e) Press apples to make cider.
3. Ask students to find out what their grandparents' first names are (were) and to report them to the class. Compile a list of the names. Compare them with the most common names heard today.
4. Ask students to project the needs of the future in the areas of space, housing, transportation, etc. and what changes they can foresee.

Notes/Ideas for Next Time

_____
_____
_____
_____
_____
_____
_____
_____
_____
_____
_____
_____
_____
_____
_____
_____
_____
_____
_____
_____
_____
_____
_____

History

Which Is Older?

Name _____

Circle the picture (A or B) in each pair that is the oldest. On the lines below each pair, write how much you know about the items.

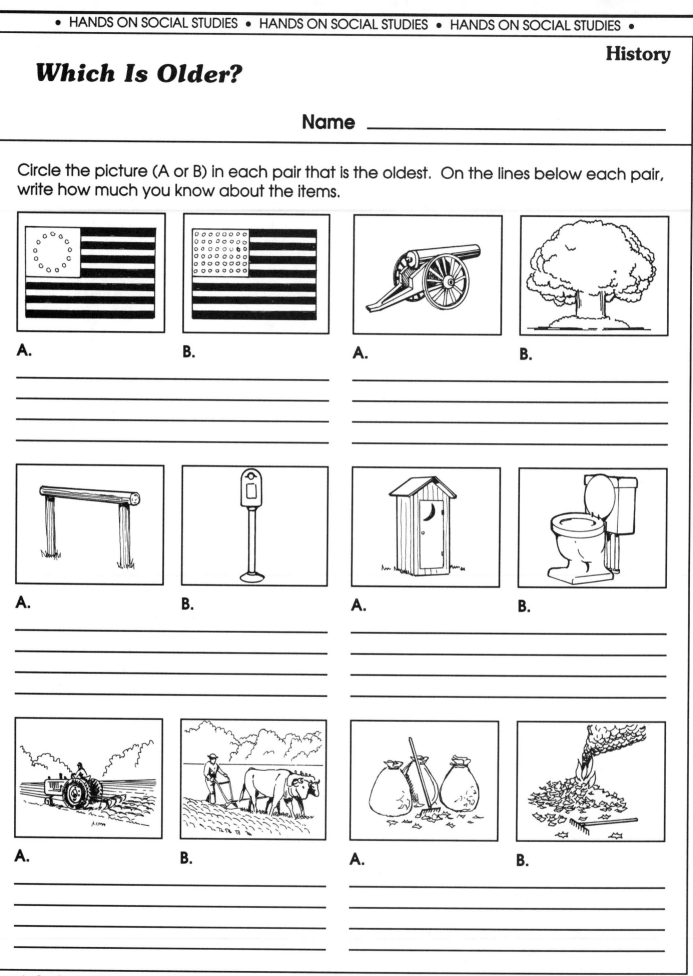

A.　　　　B.　　　　　　A.　　　　B.

_____　　　　_____
_____　　　　_____
_____　　　　_____

A.　　　　B.　　　　　　A.　　　　B.

_____　　　　_____
_____　　　　_____
_____　　　　_____

A.　　　　B.　　　　　　A.　　　　B.

_____　　　　_____
_____　　　　_____
_____　　　　_____

History

Inventions

Concepts

- Inventions have enabled us to live better and easier lives.
- An economic, military or social need may bring about an invention.
- Inventions have determined where and how people live.
- Most inventions have been beneficial; though some have been harmful.

Objectives

- To realize inventions evolve mostly out of need
- To develop a product out of need
- To develop sequencing skills

Materials

wrapping paper, paints

Vocabulary

invention, discovery

Background Information

It is said that "Rome wasn't built in a day". Nor are many things. Necessity can be the mother of invention. Inventions can be the generators of need. Some products are created due to an economic, military or social need. Additional inventions evolve and changes occur as the use of an invention demands greater efficiency.

Teaching Suggestions

- Have students think about the steps in their ability to run, scoot, creep, crawl, walk. Tell them that although the ability to run is a result of one's own physical development, it is similar to the development of many products as products also progress through adjustments or stages. Also, just as running is not

necessarily the last stage in physical movement, a product's current stage is not necessarily its last. It can often be improved or produced in another form.

- Tell students that down through history, inventions have changed the ways people live. For example, thousands of years ago, people had to hunt for animals and gather wild plants. They had to move about to find food.

Draw a horizontal line. Write "hunt, gather, travel" on the left side of the line and write "today's food procurement" on the right side. Ask students how we get our food today. Write their responses under "procurement". Ask students what happened in between to make these differences. List their responses down through the middle of the line. At this time, pay no attention to order. (Possible responses: planting, raising, trading, selling, manufacturing, transportation, canning, processing, etc.)

- Divide students into small groups. Have each group research a step named in the growth of food procurement. When the research is completed, tell students to sit along a line in the floor in the order of each step. Roll out a sheet of wrapping paper. Divide it into the number of groups (steps) you have. Assign a section to each group in order. Tell each group to paint a picture of their step in food procurement. (This could be done with many products.)

- Have students list inventions they know about or give them a list of inventions. Have each student select an invention and write a report about it.

- With the class, list some problems or needs that will affect the human race (ie: pollution, health, space travel, waste, energy, etc.). Be specific. Distribute page 68, *Inventions*. Tell students to select one of the problems that they just listed, or one of their own, and have them complete the activity sheet. Explain that they will have to read about the problem to understand it. Then, tell them to apply what they learn to the creation of a product to rectify the problem. They should be creative. They should not be concerned about the technology. (Scientists combine their technical knowledge with creativity when they produce an invention.) This activity could be done in small groups. One step beyond: Have students make prototypes of their inventions and demonstrate them to the group.

Notes/Ideas for Next Time

_____
_____
_____
_____
_____
_____
_____
_____
_____

Inventions

History

Name _____

Name a problem. _____

An inventor needs to have an understanding of a problem and an ability to create a device that will alleviate or reduce the problem. Research the problem named above so you will know all you can about it and will be better able to answer the questions below and "invent" a device to eliminate or reduce the problem.

Describe precisely what the problem is. _____

_____

_____

_____

What needs to be done about the problem? _____

_____

_____

_____

Tell how you would do what needs to be done to alleviate or reduce the problem. Tell how your device would work.

_____

_____

_____

_____

_____

_____

_____

_____

_____

_____

_____

_____

_____

_____

Draw a picture of your device to the right.
Label its parts.

History

Industrial Revolution

Concepts

- The Industrial Revolution was responsible for great changes in the ways people lived.
- The Industrial Revolution increased production of many goods and services.

Objectives

- To understand what workers have gone through to get where they are today
- To see that working together is more efficient than working individually

Vocabulary

industrialization, guilds, textiles, unions

Preparation

- Make arrangements to take your class to a factory. Visit it before the whole class goes to be sure it is safe and to learn about its manufacturing features.
- Gather simple craft books (ie: clothing, food, textiles, embroidery, weaving, woodworking, candle-making, soap-making, etc.). Ask the school and/or community librarian to contribute to the collection.
- Cut 9" x 12" sheets of paper into six pieces (6 - 4" x 4 1/2"). Cut enough 4" x 4 1/2" pieces so that every student will get the same number of pieces (the number of students in the class). Make as many stacks of paper as you have students. Put as many pieces of paper in each stack as you have students.
- Write a letter home explaining that students will be making an old-fashioned craft. The students will be responsible for

bringing the materials they will need. The students may need some help from home. Ask for volunteers at school if you want them or ask parents to help their child at home.

Background Information

By the mid-1800's, industrialization had become widespread in Western Europe and in the northeastern United States. It changed the lives and work of the people. Before the Industrial Revolution, most manufacturing was done by hand, at home or in small workshops. However, with the revolution, manufacturing moved out of the home and workshops and into factories with power-driven machines.

Teaching Suggestions

- Begin this activity with a field trip through a factory that is set up to take school children on tours.
- Tell students about the upcoming trip. Make a list with them of things they want to look for and/or questions they want answered.
- After the trip, ask students what they thought of the trip, what they think people did before _____ (name of product) was manufactured, and what opinions they formed. Have them write thank you letters to the factory personnel telling them what they most enjoyed about the trip.
- Assuming the class has been learning about the Industrial Revolution, have a discussion about it. Ask the following questions or similar ones to stimulate the discussion.

1. What is the difference between work at home and work in a factory?
2. What were some good things about the Industrial Revolution?
3. What unfavorable things have occurred over the years as a result of industrialization?
4. What are some unpleasant working conditions that often occur?
5. How do workers show displeasure about poor working conditions?
6. Who fights for workers? How?
7. Who benefitted as a result of the Industrial Revolution? How did they benefit?
8. What effect did the simultaneous growth of transportation, along with the Industrial Revolution, have on society? What would have happened without it?
9. When and where did the Industrial Revolution take place?

- Draw a Venn diagram on the board. Two interlocking circles are drawn. The topics to be compared are written above the circles. The left circle's area that does not touch the right, and the right circle's area that does not touch the left, contain statements that tell how the topics are different. The area where the two circles overlap contains statements that are the same about both topics. Two interesting topics might be manufacturing before the Industrial Revolution and manufacturing after the Industrial Revolution.

- Division of Labor
  1. Give each student a stack of 4" x 4 1/2" pieces of paper.

History

Industrial Revolution continued

Each student should receive as many pieces of paper as there are students in the class. Tell them to number each piece of paper in order.

2. Collect the papers. Put all the 1's together, 2's together, etc. Put the stacks in numerical order on a table.

3. Have students line up before the #1 stack. Tell each student to go through the line and pick up a piece of paper from each stack and to put them in numerical order. When they have one from each stack, they should put the stack down at the end of the table the stacks are on and go to their seats. Time students, but do not tell them that you are timing them.

4. Do #2 again.

5. This time, have every student stand behind a stack. Have the students behind the 1's stack take a piece of paper from the stack and hand it to the student behind the 2's stack. Have the student behind the 2's stack add page 2 and pass it to the student behind the 3's stack, and so on until the end of the line. The last person will make a stack and set it down. Repeat this mass production until all the pages are in ordered stacks. Time students again.

6. Ask students which way they believe was the most efficient. Then, reveal the timed results.

• Have students look at craft books and select one they would like to make. Tell them they will be responsible for getting the materials they will need. Send home a letter explaining the project (see Preparation). You may want students to work on their crafts at school and/or home. When they are finished, have them tell how their craft is manufactured today.

A culminating activity: Have a craft fair. Display the students' work.

• Distribute page 72, *The Industrial Revolution*. Have students draw a picture for each frame and write a sentence about each one.

History

The Renaissance

Concepts

• The Renaissance was an era of change and rebirth.
• Many great men made lasting contributions to humanity during the Renaissance.
• Renaissance men and women were interested in improving their lives and developing their talents to the fullest.

Objectives

• To understand that the Renaissance was a period of time in which great, and lasting, change took place
• To have a sense of what life was like during the Renaissance
• To know about some of the great Renaissance men

Vocabulary

Renaissance, humanity, fresco, humanists, classical antiquity, philosophy

Preparation

• Obtain reproductions of Greek, Roman, Medieval and Renaissance paintings and sculptures (postcards, textbooks, etc.).
• Obtain recordings of an Italian opera or two.
• Arrange for a guided tour at an art museum of the Renaissance period.

Background Information

The Renaissance was a new way of life that began in Italy in the early 14th century. It spread to other European countries and lasted until about the beginning of the 17th century. Although Renaissance means rebirth, the Italians did not think they were doing anything new. The Italians studied the learning and art of ancient Greece and Rome, called classical antiquity, because they felt that ancient culture was what they wanted to model their lives after. The outcome of their studies resulted in a new culture which many believe began the modern era of human history.

History

The Renaissance continued

Though Renaissance men and women wanted to relive classical antiquity, they also wanted to improve their lives and develop their talents to the fullest and achieve excellence both physically and mentally. They looked at themselves and the world around them differently than they ever had before. Greater attention was given to the study of humanity. Scholars and artists, called humanists, studied literature and philosophy to understand humanity. Artists' work involved more human characteristics. Writers who studied the ancient languages began to write biographies and poetry in Italian. Musicians created versions of Greek tragedy which became operas. Some scientists did research and developed Greek medical and scientific theories and went on to discover more. The people of Renaissance times believed that through understanding classical antiquity, they would have better lives.

Teaching Suggestions

● Look at Renaissance architecture. Make your classroom appear to have the feeling of the period by putting up pictures characteristic of the Renaissance period, cut-out gold columns, heavy brocadelike materials, mosaics, etc.

Go on a guided tour of an art museum. Do the above activity as a preparation for the trip.

● Upon return from the trip to the museum, have students draw something they saw on the guided tour. Add their drawings to the Renaissance environment you created.

● Have students work in groups of three or four. Have them do one or both of the following:
1. Dress as one of the pictures they saw at the museum. Have them bring it to life by writing a skit and acting it out.
2. Make a diorama of one of the pictures they saw at the museum.

● Tell students that the attempts of Florentine musicians to create versions of Greek tragedy turned into famous Italian opera. Tell them briefly the story of an Italian opera and let them listen to the opera (or a part of it).

● Tell students that there were many great Renaissance men, some of whom are listed below. Have them select one of these men, research the person, and report about the person to the class.
Giovanni Bellini, Giovanni Boccacio, Borgia, Sandro Botticelli, Pieter Bruegel, Filippo Brunelleschi, Benvenuto Cellini, Da Vinci, Dante, Della Robbia, Donatello Albrecht Durer, Desiderius Erasmus, Gallileo Galilei, El Greco, Hans Hobein, Filippo Lippi, Niccolo Macchiavelli, Christopher Marlowe, Masaccio, Medici, Michelangelo Michel de Montaigne, Saint Thomas More, Petrarch, Raphael, William Shakespeare, Tintoretto, Titian

● Have students research some of Italy's large cities at the time of the Renaissance (Florence, Milan, Rome, Venice) and paint murals of the life in them. They should realize Italy was not yet a country, but consisted of about 250 states, each with a ruling city.

● Hold a discussion about life during the Renaissance. Ask some of the following questions and others of your own.
1. Why did the people at the time of the Renaissance study ancient Greece and Rome?
2. What are some things from the Renaissance that have lasted?
3. Why was Leonardo Da Vinci considered a "universal man"?
4. What was life like for children during the Renaissance?
5. What subjects were studied by the scholars?
6. How is Medieval art similar to and different from Renaissance art?
7. How did the Renaissance spread to other countries from Italy?
8. Has America had a "renaissance"? Explain.

● Distribute page 73, *The Renaissance*. The directions on them are self-explanatory. The students should complete the page independently.

Teaching Suggestions

_____
_____
_____
_____
_____
_____
_____
_____
_____

71

Industrial Revolution

Name _____

Family Life Before the Industrial Revolution

_____
_____
_____

Family Life after the Industrial Revolution

_____
_____
_____

Working Conditions During the Industrial Revolution

_____
_____
_____

Modern Working Conditions

_____
_____
_____

72

History

The Renaissance

Name _____

Study the pictures of Renaissance life below. Write a story about each one on the lines next to it.

Pioneer Life

Moving West in America

Concepts

- Pioneers faced danger and hardships.
- Pioneers had to have many skills in order to survive.
- Out of the settling of the West came many stories and traditions.

Objectives

- To understand how difficult life was on America's frontier
- To learn about some specific pioneers, events and places in the settling of America's West
- To use research skills to find specific facts

Vocabulary

pioneer, frontier, squatter, homesteader, miller, blacksmith, peddler, prospector, mountain man, circuit rider

Preparation

- Make arrangements to visit a living museum to see re-enactments of pioneer life or an art museum to see artworks and artifacts depicting life on the frontier.
- Enlist the help of the school and/or community librarian in gathering fiction and non-fiction books about settling the West.

Background Information

Though some pioneers ventured West because they craved adventure, most of them faced dangers and hardships in their quest for a new, improved life. The pioneer men carried an axe and a rifle, but the other possessions pioneer families could take were limited. They took nothing with them that could be made. The pioneers needed many skills. The men had to know how to farm, hunt, build and make the items necessary for carrying out their work. The women helped the men with farm work, cared for the children and those who were ill, prepared food on an open fire and made the cloth for the clothing they made.

The pioneers were good neighbors on the trail and in their settlements. They helped each other repair their wagons, build their homes and harvest their crops. They also shared their food and other supplies when items were scarce. The settlers would not tolerate a person who would not get along with neighbors.

Teaching Suggestions

- Ask students if they know the names of any famous frontiersmen. List them. Ask students to tell what they know about these famous people.
- Write the names of several early pioneers/frontiersmen at the top of 5" x 7" index cards (one on each card). Distribute one to every student. Tell students to write 10 facts about each person on their cards, from difficult or obscure facts to the easy and obvious ones. Then, have students present the facts to the class, one at a time, and have the class guess who the facts describe.
- Hold a class discussion about the development of the West. Ask some of the following questions or some of your own.
  1. What characteristics were helpful to a pioneer?
  2. What were some of the dangers or hardships the pioneers had to face?
  3. What were some of the routes the pioneers traveled?
  4. What were some skills useful to pioneers?
  5. How did the pioneers obtain the property on which they settled?
  6. What kind of law and order did the pioneers have?
  7. What were boom towns? ghost towns?
  8. What was life like for the children of pioneers?
  9. When a pioneer wanted a new dress, what had to be done?
  10. Describe the different frontier stages.
- Reading Activities

  Select a book about the settling of the West. Read a chapter of it to your class each day.

  Find multiple copies of a book about the settling of the West. Use it with your reading classes.

  Set up a Pioneer Life Reading Center. If possible, put it in an old wagon. Make the wagon a Conestoga or Prairie Schooner. Let students read in the center during their free time, complete a research assignment about pioneer life, and/or read a book of their choice and write a report about it.

- Have every student write one true statement and one false statement about the settling of the West. Select about thirty of them and make a worksheet for the class to do.
- On an index card, put the name of a trail, act or ordinance, frontier town or event (ie: El Camino Real, Northwest Ordinance, Santa

Moving West in America continued

Fe, gold rush, etc.) that had something to do with the settling of the West. Give one to each student. Have them write three facts about the item written at the top of the card and report the facts to the class.

- Sing ballads of the West. Listen to some music with western themes like "Oklahoma", "Rodeo" or the "Grand Canyon Suite".

- Read Henry Wadsworth Longfellow's poem "The Village Blacksmith" to the class and discuss it together. Explain that the blacksmith was just one of several professionals who lived in America's frontier towns or who had something to do with settling America's frontiers. List some of the others on the board and discuss their roles: scout, mountain man, cowboy, homesteader, peddler, circuit rider, outlaw, sheriff, prospector, stagecoach driver, miller, fur trader, soldier, Pony Express rider, Indian, trail blazer.

  Tell students to select one of the early people on the frontier and to write a poem about that person.

- Plan a field trip to a living museum to see the re-enactment of pioneer life or to an art museum to see art depicting the westward movement in life or to an art museum to see art depicting the westward movement in America (ie: Remington, Russell, Curtis, etc.).

- Peddlers who traveled from one frontier town to another not only had wares to sell, but they had stories to tell. Have

students become story tellers and tell about some of the accomplishments and feats (ie: Mike Fink and Pecos Bill) of the early settlers.

- Have students write an additional verse to a familiar song like "Home on the Range".

- Have students put on a "Wild West Show". Invite families or other classes to see it.

- Distribute copies of page 76, *Moving West in America*. Students can use books from the Pioneer Life Reading Center to complete the sentences. Have them share their sentences with the class.

Notes/Ideas for Next Time

Moving West in America

History

Name _____

Complete the sentences below to make true statements about America's frontier life.

As the pioneers moved west, _____
_____

Until the railroad crossed the country, _____
_____

Life on the frontier _____
_____

When the pioneers reached where they wanted to settle, _____
_____

Caravans of wagons _____
_____

Every pioneer had _____
_____

Brave pioneers dreamed of _____
_____

On the Oregon Trail _____
_____

The rush to California _____
_____

The first pioneers to cross the country were _____
_____

Neighbors on the frontier _____
_____

Pioneer boys and girls _____
_____

Pack animals and livestock _____
_____

The Homestead Act of 1862 _____
_____

For entertainment, frontier families _____
_____

The pioneers had to know _____
_____

76   ©MCMXCIII Instructional Fair, Inc.

A Perspective from the Inside and Out

Health/ Medicine

Concepts

- AIDS is spread through contact with infected body fluids.
- Though some groups of people are more infected with the disease than others, all groups of people are susceptible.

Objectives

- To understand how AIDS is transmitted
- To develop personal responsibility for one's health
- To develop an understanding for those infected with the virus

Vocabulary

immune, semen, fatal, vaccine, homosexual, bisexual, intravenous, hemophiliac

Background Information

AIDS is the advanced form of the Human Immunodeficiency Virus (HIV) which may exist within an infected person a long time before he/she shows any symptoms. An infected person may spread the disease without having AIDS.

AIDS was an unknown disease in the United States before the first case was reported in 1981. By April of 1992, 218,301 people had been diagnosed with it. The disease affects the body's immune system, which means the person infected with the illness is susceptible to other diseases.

No one at this time has been cured of AIDS, but medical researchers are working fervently to find a cure.

Teaching Suggestions

How much of this activity you use with your class will depend on its composition. In some cases, this unit might be used to teach an awareness of the disease. In other cases, where students are more exposed to, or participate in, activities that are believed to spread the disease, this unit might be used to teach appropriate behaviors.

- Write AIDS on the board. Ask students if they know what this acronym means (Acquired Immune Deficiency Syndrome).
- Ask students what they know about AIDS. List what they know or believe about the illness, true or false. Discuss the list with them. Cross out false assumptions.
- Help students understand that AIDS is caused by the spread of HIV (Human Immunodeficiency Virus) which may exist within a person's body who doesn't show any of the AIDS symptoms.
- Discuss how AIDS can be transmitted: which victims are innocent recipients and which enter into activities of high risk.
- Have students bring in news articles about AIDS.
- Discuss precautionary measures (dentists, hospitals, social contacts, etc.).
- Discuss what is being done to help AIDS patients.
- Invite a medical professional to speak to the class.
- Pass out copies of page 78, *A Perspective from the Inside Out.* Have students complete it independently. Discuss it as a class once students have finished it.

Notes/Ideas for Next Time

_____
_____
_____
_____
_____
_____
_____
_____
_____
_____
_____
_____
_____
_____
_____
_____
_____
_____
_____
_____
_____
_____
_____
_____
_____
_____
_____
_____

A Perspective from the Inside and Out

Health/ Medicine

Name _____

Read the following situation, and then do as directed.

Casey is a twelve-year-old hemophiliac. He received a blood transfusion two years ago. Apparently, the blood he received was infected with HIV. Now, Casey has been diagnosed as carrying the virus. The school board in Casey's school district has a dilemma. They are under pressure from some of the parents not to allow Casey to attend school with his classmates. Casey's parents and others think Casey should have a normal education.

Write a letter to the school board stating your opinion and reasons for it.

_____

_____

_____

_____

_____

_____

_____

_____

_____

_____

_____

_____

_____

Write a letter from Casey's point of view. _____

_____

_____

_____

_____

_____

_____

_____

_____

_____

78

Working Alone or Together

Concepts

- The Declaration of Independence declared America free from British rule.
- The Declaration of Independence made America a nation equal with all others.
- The Declaration of Independence states that all people have certain rights.

Objectives

- To understand why the Declaration of Indepedence was written
- To understand that people have a say in who runs America's government
- To understand that every country is autonomous and still has a good working relationship with others
- To understand that some things are best accomplished working together

Vocabulary

monarchy, democracy, dictatorship, co-existence, republic

Preparation

- Make copies of the Declaration of Independence for every student.
- If possible, obtain a replica of the Declaration to display. Make a patriotic bulletin board. Make the document its main attraction.

Background Information

There had been growing animosity between England and America several years before the Declaration of Independence was adopted. The American colonists wanted to make decisions that affected them, and they resented England's heavy taxation on imported goods. Though England and America were already at war over these issues, American patriots felt it was necessary to verbalize a break from England. The Continental Congress appointed a committee of five, headed by Thomas Jefferson, to draw up such a document. The Declaration of Independence was adopted July 4, 1776. Ever since, July 4th is celebrated as America's birthday.

Teaching Suggestions

- Give every student a copy of the Declaration of Independence. Read through it together. Through discussion, help students understand its meaning.
- Compare the set-up of America's government with England's (and other countries of your choosing).
- Ask if students believe that the United States and/or other countries are better off being completely independent, if they need each other, or if the stronger nations should rule the weaker ones.
- Make three lists: one with advantages of being a country completely independent, one with advantages of countries working together, and one for stronger nations ruling weaker, developing countries.
- Discuss the role the United Nations has played in recent events (Desert Storm, Somalia, etc.). Ask how they think the countries involved felt. Should every country declare itself independent? Does the United States practice what it preaches?
- Look at other current world situations. Ask if we should get involved.
- Ask students to imagine what the United States might be like today if England still made its laws. Imagine America with a king.

Notes/Ideas for Next Time

_____
_____
_____
_____
_____
_____
_____
_____
_____
_____
_____
_____
_____
_____
_____
_____
_____
_____
_____
_____
_____
_____
_____
_____
_____

Working Alone and Together

Name _____

List some things you have accomplished alone. _____

_____
_____
_____
_____
_____

From the list above, select one thing that you wish you could have done with someone else and why. _____

_____
_____

List some things you have accomplished working with others. _____

_____
_____
_____
_____
_____

From the list above, select one thing that you could not have done alone and tell why.

_____
_____
_____

Do you think it is always necessary to have someone give directions and set rules?
_____ If your answer is yes, why and when? If no, why not? _____

_____
_____
_____
_____

Think of one situation where you feel there is too much authority over you. Write a mini declaration of independence. _____

_____
_____
_____
_____